Praise for *The Ultimate Manual: The Missing Guide to Living a Meaningful Life* by Craig C. Sroda

"Craig Sroda is a magnificent curator of the best thinking in personal and professional development, and he brilliantly synthesizes the best of the best to create this accessible manual for anyone wanting to get and stay on purpose. Roll up your sleeves, digest every page, and complete every worksheet because everything in this book has been created with thoughtfulness and heart. Use it to create a happier, sweeter, more productive, and success-filled life!"

—**MICKEY HAY, PH.D. AND ERIN CRESSY, PH.D.**,
Leadership Consultants at Cressy Consulting

"I've personally experienced working with Craig as he coached me through the life plan process. You will go through that same process with Craig in this book as he guides you through the steps that will lead to more clarity and intention for you and your life. This truly is the "Ultimate Manual" for taking a proactive approach to learning about yourself and how that understanding can change your life."

—**SCOTT FRANKO**,
Founder, Designer, Author, and Speaker at Franko Design

"Craig Sroda has truly put together the "ultimate manual" for anyone looking for an impactful yet simple guide to creating a life plan. Pulling from free tools and resources on the web, he walks you through in a step-by-step fashion a process to learn about yourself and gain clarity on what you want in life and most importantly how to go about getting it. Whether you're a seasoned professional needing a restart, a stay-at-home parent thinking about what's next, or a recent college graduate, Craig's *Ultimate Manual* is for you!"

—**TIM LEMAN**, CEO at Gibson,
Author of *rEvolution: Turn Crisis Into Clarity and Ignite Growth*

THE
ULTIMATE
MANUAL

the MISSING GUIDE
to LIVING
MEANINGFUL LIFE

CRAIG C. SRODA

Visit **www.craigsroda.com** *for support with your journey through this manual.*

This Ultimate Manual belongs to:

_____

On this day of _____ ,
*I hereby promise myself to **start living with intention!***
I will work through this manual at my own pace,
*getting to know my **true self** and **purpose** in this lifetime.*
I make the commitment to live my life to the fullest!

Signed _____

CONTENTS

PART 1

TRUTH

WHO YOU ARE
AND HOW YOU GOT HERE

JAMES 1:5

*If any of you lacks wisdom, you should ask God, who gives generously
to all without finding fault, and it will be given to you.*

MATTHEW 7:7

*Ask and it will be given to you; seek and you will find;
knock and the door will be opened to you.*

THE MOST IMPORTANT thing you can do for yourself and the people you care about is to know the truth about who you are and how you became who you are. Wrapped up in that knowledge is everything you believe, your mission in life, and the ways you will deal with all the sorts of unpleasantries thrown at you . . . and how you will accept or reject the opportunities served up to you on a silver platter. You must get an inside-out perspective of Self that resonates as true and complete. That is an inside and individual job, and the purpose and goal of Part 1 of this workbook is to help you do it. No one can do it for you, so take the time to do this for you.

Understanding what your natural behaviors and strengths are, while being honest about your weaknesses, is part of that journey to the True You. I feel knowing what you are passionate about and what is important to you is probably the best gift you can give to yourself. Mapping out where you are going to go in the next part of your life as an individual is first about knowing where you have come from and how you became who you are right now. That gives you clarity about where you are right now, and that's important because today is the launching pad you leap from into tomorrow.

I suggest that you do the exercises in this program entirely on your own (no help from others, please, and no asking others' opinions) — on your own in a time of quiet, keeping notes of your results. I have included lots of charts with spaces for notes. Discover yourself through your responses. Only then can you imagine and achieve your Life Plan.

NOTE:
As you do this work, you may feel supported by going to my website, **www.craigsroda.com**, and reading my blog posts on many of the topics presented in this workbook.

CHAPTER 1

SELF-AWARENESS,
OR HIDING IN PLAIN SIGHT

YOU WOULD THINK that since we have had millennia to observe each other and ourselves, that the easiest thing humans would ever do is understand who and how we are — and why. You'd think it would be a piece of cake to know how to change ourselves if we are unhappy with who or how we are. The truth of the matter? We treat that knowledge as if it is the one secret of the world that is forever hidden from us.

We are conscious beings, filled with feelings, thoughts, and plenty of mental pictures (at their best called daydreams and at their worst called nightmares). This consciousness provides us with awareness of our bodies, the physical things in our world and awareness of other individuals. This consciousness also gives us our personal interpretations of things: our unique perspective and opinions of events of the world and our judgments about the behaviors of others, and our preferred (and comfortable) ways of doing things. Awareness also gives us internal tools that we all carry around with us to make our way out in the world among people — in other words, our tools of survival.

You can know yourself much, much better than you do right now. This new knowledge I'll be helping you acquire gives you a solid foundation for building your Life Plan and walking forward into a new future as you achieve it.

What's Coming Up

In this first part of the book, I'm going to put you to work doing some simple exercises that better reveal to you who and how you are. These are exercises that might involve personal reflection and introspection and you need to make time for it. Please prefer quiet time — no television or people milling around you. It's what you must call 'me time.'

You will get an understanding of your personal strengths (and thus a few of your weaknesses). You will have a look at how you are doing today in the core areas of your life (I will help you identify those). You'll be looking at your emotional intelligence (or EQ) through a short quiz on EQ along with one called DISC, which will reveal your usual preferred behaviors, reactions, expectations and motivations (and how they shift and change with circumstances) as well as view your strengths and weaknesses from another perspective. And — since this is a life planning book that we are putting in the hands of people who have relationships with people — you will also be looking at your personal language of love (how you seek love from and express love to your spouse or partner, children, friends, associates . . . even strangers).

I had done many of these assessments and questionnaires as part of my professional life before becoming a life coach, but I didn't hesitate to do them again for this life planning purpose. The eye-opening exercise for me was the one on the *language of love.* I simply didn't know my love language until I did that exercise! It has radically increased my comfort in all relationships. So, guys — do not be macho. Ladies, do not be dismissive. Don't any of you think that you are exempt from any of these exercises for any reason! Each of them holds some astonishing self-knowledge for you and some terrific Ah-Ha insights about the dynamics in your various relationships.

CHAPTER 2

YOUR STRENGTHS

*"It takes far less energy to move from first-rate performance to excellence
than it does to move from incompetence to mediocrity."*

PETER DRUCKER

ASK AN OLDER teenager what his strengths are. Be prepared for a blank look. Anyone who is already earning his living, in a committed relationship, or raising a family, however, should have a better idea of what some of his personal strengths are. You would think so, anyway — but that is not always the case. And that is the purpose of this next section which holds your first life-planning and self-awareness exercises.

What do we mean by ***strengths?*** It is basically what you naturally do best. It's what your greatest talent might be. Some people call it their forte. It might be the way you explain who you are to other people. Think about people you know in terms of their strength. You might say that George is the consummate organizer. Organization is one of George's strengths. Marianne might be a brilliant conversationalist, able to draw people out and get them chatting, listening attentively, participating attentively in the conversation. That is her strength.

What do we mean by **strengths?** *It is basically what you naturally do best.*

The StrengthsFinder Concept

The Clifton StrengthsFinder which I ask you to use is based on research revealing that we each 'find ourselves' within 34 core strengths. They help us identify how we see the world and how we are enabled to move through it. Of the 34 potential strengths, we each have our **'top 5'** — those core strengths which dominate our personalities and how we take action. They energize us, and help us be productive in our unique way. Generally speaking, our top 5 strengths don't change much over time; they are our motors throughout life.

Develop Your Strengths

An unwitting teacher might ask a student to identify, admit to and focus on his greatest **weakness** with the goal of turning it into a strength. Almost all experts in personal development now disagree with that approach! In fact, it sounds like punishment . . . Just as Peter Drucker has said, people are more motivated to *excel* in something they're already *good* at.

I encourage you to develop your strengths (because you'll succeed at it), but *be aware* of your glaring weaknesses and how to minimize their impact and presence, since they can potentially sabotage your positive efforts at growth and change.

Let's look at this with a keyboarding example. Lots of people use computer keyboards, but not everyone types with all 10 fingers at great speed with 100% accuracy. For many, typing with two fingers of each hand is a great achievement — and it is all they need for their emails and social media and comparative shopping on the web. It's only a weakness in comparison with an executive assistant who uses all 10 fingers that fly across the keyboard for hours on end with 99% accuracy. Why would you expend energy and time on moving from 2-finger typing to 10-finger professional speed? If you don't earn your living on the keyboard, you don't have the motivation to do so. But the executive assistant does. Developing that strength gives her not only mastery, but control over a marketable skill. For her to develop that strength even further by, for instance, learning software macros that insert entire pages of content at a keystroke matters a great deal to her for her earning power and employability.

Exercise: StrengthsFinder

This assessment is called **StrengthsFinder 2.0** from Clifton/Gallup Research. Here are the steps to taking the assessment.

   NOTE: This is the only assessment I recommend in this program that will cost anything — therefore, I make it optional. I think it is important, as there is nothing else quite like it on the marketplace of 'strength' assessing. However, if it's not in your current budget, feel free to skip this and come back to it later.

Exercise: 5 Key Strengths

1. Go to www.strengthsfinder.com
2. Sign up to take the assessment.
3. Set up an account.
4. Take the assessment.
5. Review your results by signing into the Strengths Finder portal at http://strengths.gallup.com
6. Digitally save or print your results.
   a. Go to Reports
   b. View and Print — Strengths Insight and Action-Planning Guide
   c. View and Print — Strengths Insight Guide

When you have done the assessment, fill in your **top 5 strengths** and their descriptions as you understand them in the box below.

Strengths	Description
1.	
2.	
3.	
4.	
5.	

Exercise: 16 Personalities

This second questionnaire or assessment is called **16 Personalities**. It presents a markedly different but very useful way to understand your strengths. Here are the steps to taking the assessment.

1. Go to www.16personalities.com
2. Do the assessment questionnaire
3. Click to your results page and read about your Type
4. Click on the Strengths and Weaknesses link on the left under Explore Your Type
5. Read about your strengths, but also about your weaknesses

When you have done the assessment, fill in your **top strengths** and their descriptions as you understand them in the box below.

Strengths	Description

Now, as I will ask you to do in most chapters, fill in the box below by responding to questions about the two exercises you have just completed.

Your Key Learnings — StrengthsFinder

What did you learn?

_____

_____

_____

_____

_____

What stood out?

_____

_____

_____

_____

_____

What was a surprise?

_____

_____

_____

_____

_____

What is in question?

_____

_____

_____

_____

_____

Key Learnings — The 16 Personalities

What did you learn?

_____

_____

_____

_____

_____

_____

What stood out?

_____

_____

_____

_____

_____

What was a surprise?

_____

_____

_____

_____

_____

What is in question?

_____

_____

_____

_____

_____

CHAPTER 3

EQ, OR EMOTIONAL INTELLIGENCE AND RELATIONSHIPS

"Where we have strong emotions, we're liable to fool ourselves."

CARL SAGAN

Life Is Only Relationship

I HAVE TO state the obvious here: *Life is all about relationships.*

From the relationships most distant from us to the ones closest to us, it is your personal job to improve them all by starting with yourself. You are the key, the linchpin, the pivotal person in all your relationships. It stands to reason that by changing yourself, you will change the quality of all your relationships!

We have relationships with strangers every day — our political representatives and government workers whom we never or rarely even meet, those store clerks we will see only intermittently, people we pass in the street or see in the bus or observe behind the wheel of their cars and will never see again. We say we have relationships with these individuals, because, somewhere in our mind, we have an opinion or judgment about them, even in that fleeting time of connection.

We have relationships with the people we work with. These are our bosses or our supervised employees. They are vendors or customers.

Contrary to the above types of relationships which we haven't really participated in choosing, we have relationships we have consciously chosen. They are called friends, associates or business partners. They are called the boyfriend, girlfriend, life partner and spouse. We have much closer relationships and involvement with the people we call family — spouse or life partner, parents and children and so on.

There is a theory going around about how we turn into or become the _average_ of the 5 people we spend the most time with. We tend, goes the theory, to adopt those five individuals' habits, beliefs, attitudes and standards — and somehow make our own 'average' mix of them all. This theory is why top personal growth or success coaches encourage those who would be _rich_ to hang out with _rich_ people. It is why therapists advise drug and alcohol addicts who are in recovery ('clean' or 'dry') to get new friends, new work, new surroundings, new hobbies, new skills. Or, if you want to be great at a certain skill like skiing, you hang around the _best_ skiers and mimic them and all their movements. This theory is also why gang members talk, dress and behave alike, and get in trouble in the same ways — they have adopted the average of each other's habits, beliefs, attitudes and standards.

You can take this even further if you have 20-year-old (or longer) relationships behind you. Ponder the relationships you have had, but now in 10-year increments. How you have influenced each other during that decade — for better or for worse — may surprise you. How did you fare in relation to those friends during that time? If you were making a conscious effort at growth, improvement and change during that decade, did you leave those 5 people behind or did they grow with you? My clients are often awakened when they think about that! If it is time for you to make a change, or a new set of changes, I'm here to guide you.

Our **very closest relationship**, however, should not surprise you: It is your relationship with yourself. With _Self_. How very many of us are not happy with Self! And this leads us to talking about the real influence on your life of those 5 friends of yours, and then **EQ**, or Emotional Intelligence.

Our very closest relationship is with Self.

Exercise: The 5 Friends

Think deeply about the following questions and write out your answers. It is my experience that many days from now, different or additional responses will also come to you, as your subconscious mind remembers things from the past. Write it all down!

1. Who do you spend the most time with in your private life? Name those 5 people.

2. Are you adopting their habits? Which ones can you name? Think of each of those 5 people as you answer.

3. Are you adopting their belief system? Name shared beliefs. Think about the beliefs on politics, religion, work and how much you can earn, education and how much you need, treatment of others, self-esteem (and more) of each of those 5 people as you answer.

4. Are your standards — of things like honesty, industriousness, perseverance, earnings, respect for others (and more) — influenced to be higher or lower than your own natural tendency? Name how the five friends set their bar, and how you mimic them.

What EQ Is

Let's make a distinction straight out of the gate between IQ and EQ. IQ is an academic test of *brain smarts*. EQ is all about your *emotional smarts*. The Intelligence Quotient versus the Emotional Quotient. They are two real, but very different, aspects of who you are.

Think about 'emotions and feelings' as a concept for a moment. However we express them (or let them burst out of control), stuff them down or go into denial about them, there is one thing we can say about emotions which is true of all human beings:

We all _have an overabundance of emotions and feelings_.

Another thing we can say about emotions? Most of us _don't know what to do with them_! Rest easy. Looking at, and then developing, your Emotional Intelligence is where you start.

In the world of work and leadership, high EQ is in fact taking over from high IQ as a way of hiring employees. How does that work? It used to be that businesses hired managers and executives (not to mention all the other jobs) for the person's brain smarts — what they knew about business, finance, their specific field of expertise or skills, etc., and what kind of vocational or college degree they had (because they had to have one, right?). EQ, however, is being seen as far more effective in helping people build teams and get the people in them to work together happily, productively and efficiently — *intelligently* — to achieve a shared business goal and improve their company's profitability. After all, that is what business is all about.

In families and couples, business partnerships and all kinds of relationships, EQ is important, too — we would say it is vital information and self-knowledge that you must acquire and try to develop. It is not a 'once and done' exercise in learning, but more about awareness and continuous vigilance.

Here are five ways EQ works in all types of relationships you engage in.

Self-Awareness

You recognize your own emotions and how they affect your thoughts and behavior. You know your emotional strengths and weaknesses. You gain self-confidence and confidence around others. Once you have acquired that, you can see emotions in others and how it affects them . . . and their relationships with you and others.

Self-Regulation

A greater EQ helps you control your impulsive feelings and behaviors, both desirable and unwanted. You self-manage your feelings in healthy ways. You can take initiative from self-management of your own feelings. You follow through on commitments more comfortably. You know better how to adapt to changing circumstances.

Social Skills and Awareness

You can understand the emotions, needs, and concerns of other people, pick up on emotional cues they are broadcasting (and respond appropriately), feel more comfortable socially, and recognize the power dynamics in a group or organization . . . or in your family.

Relationship Management

You know better how to approach people to just chat, or to develop a connection with them. Strong EQ helps you have that good connection right away, communicate more clearly, inspire and influence others, work better in teams or pairs, and nip conflict in the bud.

Empathy

You have a better ability to 'relate' to others. EQ is your ability to identify with others and put yourself in their shoes. As you develop a greater Emotional Intelligence, you can recognize your own emotional state and the emotional states of others, and engage with people in a way that draws them to you.

Now Evaluate

How are you doing in the above areas in all types of relationships? Your present degree or level of Emotional Intelligence is important to grasp because it is your starting point for making improvements.

EQ is visible, but it is also hidden:
- Your EQ or lack of it affects your performance at work and interactions with all those people.
- EQ affects your physical and mental health, because all types of stress, negativity and unhappiness are simply poured into your body and mind.
- Your level of EQ, high or low, affects all the various types of relationships you engage in, whether you know it (or admit it) or not!

Without further ado, let's get you taking an EQ assessment.

Exercise: Emotional Intelligence Quotient Assessment

There are many tests for EQ. The key is to take a few and get a rating from each one on how self-aware and aware of others you truly are, and compare the types of reports they give you. Try these tests (and any other you are familiar with or find online) and document your results.

> **Here are the steps to taking the assessment:**
>
> 1. Go to either:
>   • http://www.ihhp.com/free-eq-quiz/
>   • http://testyourself.psychtests.com/testid/3038
> 2. Complete the assessment.
> 3. Write out your results.
>
> Now go to the chart on the next page to summarize what you learned from the two exercises of this section.

Key Learnings — 5 Friends

What did you learn?

_____

_____

_____

_____

_____

_____

_____

What stood out?

_____

_____

_____

_____

_____

What was a surprise?

_____

_____

_____

_____

_____

What is in question?

_____

_____

_____

_____

_____

Key Learnings — Emotional Intelligence

What did you learn?

_____

_____

_____

_____

_____

_____

What stood out?

_____

_____

_____

_____

_____

What was a surprise?

_____

_____

_____

_____

_____

What is in question?

_____

_____

_____

_____

_____

CHAPTER 4

DISC ASSESSMENT

"Do not let the behavior of others destroy your inner peace."

THE DALAI LAMA

SO FAR, YOU have discovered your **Top 5 Strengths** and completed the **16 Personalities** assessment. You have seen where you stand with your **5 Closest Friends** and with **Emotional Intelligence** today via these exercises and assessments. We want to stress that word *today*. These assessments measure these aspects of who and how you are *today*. As we move along in this Life Planning process, you will be making some decisions about new learning or training, new directions that you wish to take. Where you are *today* is your launching pad for those changes and those new goals.

There is another brilliantly insightful, scientifically proven assessment anyone can take (and by that we mean children and adults, people who work and people who never have) to help you understand why you *behave* the way you behave. It is called the **DISC** assessment.

The assessment has been around for nearly a century, and is based, firstly, on the proven premise that all human behavior is pattern-based and falls into just four categories or 'behavioral styles'. Whence the four-letter acronym of DISC, which represent the four styles/patterns of behavior. D is for dominance, I is for influence, S is for steadiness, and C is for compliance.

D is for dominance, I is for influence, S is for steadiness, and C is for compliance.

It is based, secondly, on the premise that each of us has 'usual' behaviors — those that are in play on ordinary days and in ordinary circumstances — and 'adaptive' behaviors — those that kick in when we are stressed or pressured by people or circumstances or thrown out of our comfort zone.

Each of us has our own unique combination of all **four** styles, yet one or two will typically be strong and the others less influential on our usual behaviors. What do you need to remember? No 'style' is good or bad — it just is! So, with no judgments, do a DISC assessment in the following way and note your outcomes on the 2 charts we provide in the next pages.

Exercise: Simple DISC Assessment

You are just assigning numbers to words for this exercise. In the chart on the next page, move **horizontally** and rank the four words in that **row** from 1 to 4.

- Assign a **1** to the word that is the **least like you**.
- Assign a **4** to the word that is the **most like you**.
- Then use a 2 and a 3 for the other words in that horizontal row, with **2** being **somewhat unlike you**, and **3** being **somewhat like you**.
- You will use the numbers 1, 2, 3 and 4 *one time each per row* in that way.

Thus, in the top line in the following chart where we give an **example**, we've marked 1 for 'argumentative' — meaning it is 'very unlike' or 'the least like' you! We mark 4 for 'fun-loving' — this word is the 'most like' you among the four words given on the row. 'Logical' qualifies as 'somewhat unlike' you, so we assign 2. 'Patient' qualifies as 'somewhat like' you, so we give that word a 3.

That is your **example** line. You move to the next line with the word *'forceful'* to begin the exercise for yourself, and do this for all the remaining rows of words.

You assign a number that represents your personal preferences right now, not what you think might be best (and certainly not what you think others would like you to be).

When done, add the vertical columns up, and put the number next to Total. Go to the next page and do this now.

Exercise: Simple DISC Assessment

_2_ **argumentative**	_4_ **fun-loving**	_3_ **serene**	_1_ **precise**
___ forceful	___ lively	___ modest	___ tactful
___ aggressive	___ emotional	___ accommodating	___ consistent
___ direct	___ animated	___ agreeable	___ focused
___ straightforward	___ people-focused	___ gentle	___ perfectionist
___ daring	___ impulsive	___ kind	___ cautious
___ competitive	___ expressive	___ supportive	___ precise
___ risk taker	___ talkative	___ gentle	___ factual
___ argumentative	___ fun-loving	___ patient	___ logical
___ bold	___ spontaneous	___ stable	___ organized
___ take charge	___ upbeat	___ serene	___ conscientious
___ candid	___ happy	___ loyal	___ reserved
___ independent	___ enthusiastic	___ good listener	___ high standards
___ **total**	___ **total**	___ **total**	___ **total**

When you add up the **four totals**, some will naturally be larger than others. The larger the number, the stronger that pattern of behavior for you.

Now write the letter **D** above the first (left-hand) column, **I** above the second column from the left, **S** above the third column from the left and **C** above the last (right-hand) column.

Exercise: Full DISC Assessment

There are many providers of the full DISC assessment on the marketplace, but rest assured, they all provide the same answers! For those clients of mine wanting to do a 'full' assessment, and get an explanatory report of the meaning of it all, take this next **Full DISC Assessment**, sponsored by the Tony Robbins Organization.

Here are the steps to taking the assessment:

1. Go here: www.tonyrobbins.com/disc/
2. Complete the questionnaire
3. Note your results

NOTE: In addition to the **Simple DISC Assessment** and the full Tony-Robbins-sponsored one here, feel free to go online and google other "Free DISC Assessments". There are numerous options to choose from, as it is now a well-known test done by millions of people around the world.

It is really helpful for understanding your *behavior style or pattern*, so I encourage you to take the time for it and to print out the full report (or save it as a PDF on your computer).

Make a note of your results — print them out, or have the results emailed to you for your record.

Understanding Your Results

The full DISC assessment explains the 4 behavioral styles or patterns, but for those of you doing the 'simple' version only, here is a snapshot description of each of the four behavioral styles — the 'usual' and the 'adaptive' behavior. If you had a high score for one or two of them, see if you recognize yourself in the descriptions below. If you had a lower score for some, you should still read on!

D for dominance

Usual: You like things to move fast, and without much chitchat — because you are not big on long discussions or indecisiveness. You are a do-er, a 'get it done' sort of person, and that means that you are activity-oriented (thing- or task-oriented) and you jump right in after a quick unilateral decision. You can be Directive, Domineering, Dictatorial, Dynamic, Decisive, Determined, Dogmatic, Dramatic.

Adaptive: Impatience; rude interrupting; seeking to control things (at best) and fighting to be in charge with a 'my way or the highway' attitude (at worst).

I for influence

Usual: You also like things to move fast, but you love conversation. You are a 'let's get everyone together' type of person. You are quite friendly, but not very decisive. You are gregarious and outgoing and people-oriented. This means that are a great networker. It also means that you lose track of time and what you should be doing (tasks) with that time of yours. You can be Impulsive, Impetuous, Interactive, Influential, Interested, Inspirational and Involved.

Adaptive: You spin your wheels and won't get started on the task at hand; you readily bring unhappy people together at time of conflict (so that they can 'talk it out together'), but then you just walk away thinking the reconciliation job is done.

S for steadiness

Usual: You like things to move at a predictably steady and moderate pace. You are people-oriented, and likely to ask, 'how can I help?' Long-term relationships are the most important thing to you. You are attentive to other people's feelings and opinions, and tend to be more emotional than the other behavior styles. You focus on giving everyone a chance to express themselves, which means that you are often wishy-washy when it's time to present a single decision or opinion about anything. Whatever you start, you will finish — it's starting that's the problem. You can be Steady, Supportive, Sentimental, Secretive, Sweet, Specialist, Spectator.

Adaptive: Emotional or teary; needy or clingy; seeking approval and appreciation and grumpy when it is not forthcoming; resistant to any type of immediate change without a long lead time to 'get ready'.

C for compliance

Usual: You are the slowest paced of these four styles and the most reserved around people. You also have the most focused concentration ability of the styles, and are at your happiest with details, facts, research and planning. You are a 'how are we going to do it most logically?' sort of person. You would rather be alone and work on your tasks, activities and projects in your very well thought out and planned way. You hate criticism of your work, because, after all, you are so accuracy-attentive. You're not very talkative and will often not speak at all unless asked some specific question. Before speaking, you pause and deliberately go over in your mind what the answer should be before speaking. Whatever you start, you will finish — it's finishing on someone else's schedule that's the problem. You can be Cautious, Conscientious, Critical Thinker, Compliant, Consistent, Competent, Correct.

Adaptive: Withdrawn and silent; seeking separation from noisy humans; you dig in and won't provide your share of the work to the group without long and drawn-out checking and double-checking of facts and accuracy.

Do Opposites Attract?

We often hear that 'opposites attract'. Or are they totally incompatible? From these DISC descriptions, you might notice that the D is the opposite of the S and that the I is the opposite of the C behavior style. That does not mean that the D and the S are incompatible or that the I and the C can never get along! Viva La Difference! It is what makes life so very interesting, right? Awareness of those differences (and the other's needs) is everything, and if, in your marriage or with a business partner, one of you is D and the other is S (or an I and a C), that awareness will help you respond to each other and interact on many levels in ways that are familiar and comfortable. You can get every member of your family to do the DISC assessment for fun and learning (and more harmony at home) — and companies do it all the time for many benefits.

Exercise: DISC Wrap-up

To wrap this up, in the chart below, write in the Description the specific traits or characteristics that relate to <u>your own</u> **D, I, S** or **C** style. You should have at least a couple of descriptive words in each style, even though they are not your strongest one(s). When you have done that, write out what you learned in the second, **Key Learnings,** chart.

Style	Description Applying To Me
D/Dominant	
I/Influential	
S/Steady	
C/Compliant	

Key Learnings — DISC

What did you learn?

_____

_____

_____

_____

_____

_____

What stood out?

_____

_____

_____

_____

_____

What was a surprise?

_____

_____

_____

_____

What is in question?

_____

_____

_____

_____

_____

CHAPTER 5

THE WHEEL OF LIFE

"You don't need to reinvent the wheel.
Just make sure it's not flat before you drive off into the sunset."

THE WHEEL OF LIFE is another exercise to give you real clarity on your personal starting point as you set out on a journey to create a Life Plan. Is your wheel of life 'filled' or 'flat'?

I did a little research and discovered that the Wheel of Life seems to have originated with Buddha and was used to assess an individual's inner psychological state. The Wheel has taken on a few gently different names over time, including Wheel of Balance, Wheel of Happiness and so on. Each of the names is appropriate to its purpose, as you will soon see.

The beauty of this exercise is that we look at life like we look at the wheel on a bicycle or vehicle. Just as you don't let your child take off on his bike when it's got a flat tire, and you pull over to the side of the road when your car has a flat, you don't want to roll along in life very long without 'filling the tire' if your Wheel of Life is flat!

Understanding the next exercise called the **Wheel of Life** means we need to understand what the *core areas* of our life and living are.

The basics are generally considered to be the following four core areas:

1. Health
2. Money/Career
3. Family/Friends
4. Spirituality/Religion

Sometimes one other is included to make 5 core areas, but usually not more. Could you separate finance and wealth from career and job? Sure. Likewise, in some wheels, Self-image and Community contribution are included, and in still others Leisure and Fun are on the wheel.

On the exercise starting on the next page, you see the Wheel of Life core areas that I utilize in my life coaching practice. It has eight core areas. Go ahead and do this exercise now.

Exercise: Wheel of Life

For each of the eight core areas of life shown on my preferred Wheel of Life on the next page — Career, Finances, Health, Family, Romance, Growth, Fun, and Faith — you see numbers starting on the outside at **10** and moving to the center of the wheel to **0**.

You will score each of these eight areas according to how you perceive that area of your life is going for you right now.

→ **10 is your 'top' score** for that area of your life, and that means that this area of your life is working fantastically for you right now — everything is going better than you ever could have hoped.

→ **0** is, naturally, a score you give to an area of your life where **absolutely nothing is working** for you right now — or nothing at all is happening because it is not an aspect that exists in your life right now.

Go ahead and circle the number for each core area that corresponds with how well or how poorly that area is going for you right now.

Next, draw a new circle inside the Wheel of Life by connecting all the numbers with a single line.

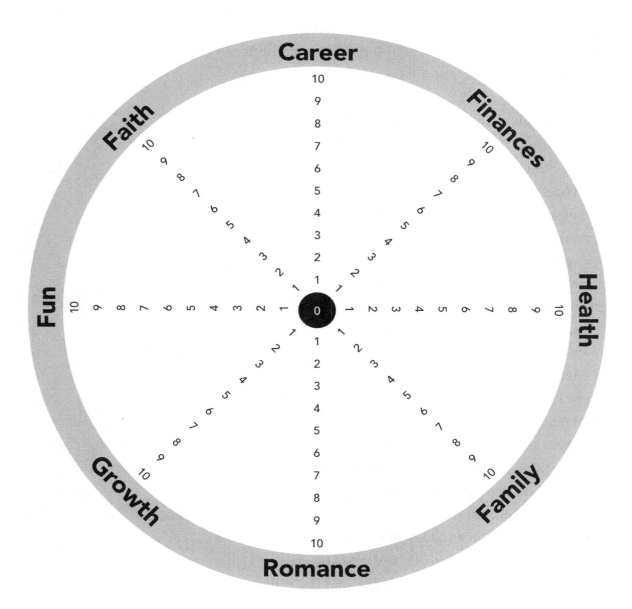

Progress, Through the Wheel of Life

Redoing this exercise over time is revealing about your progress in achieving balance. Balance means that you'll focus more on improving the struggling, 'flat-tire' core areas more, and a bit less on the 'filled-tire' areas.

This is my own, and very earliest, Wheel of Life, in the image on the right.

The thicker outer orange circle is your goal! Can you see the ***inner black line*** I drew (inside the orange circle) that represents my Wheel of Life? I ranked Family, Romance, Health and Faith quite low (compared to Finances and Growth, but also compared to the thicker outer orange circle). All four of those areas were in trouble! See also that Growth, Finances and Career — although not 10's — were much better ranked. I had thought I was doing pretty well in those areas. But . . . what about _balance_?? There I went, bumping along on a flat Wheel of Life, and I just didn't need to!

Then, as I worked through my first Life Planning process (as you are doing with this workbook), my Wheel of Life evolved, I was able to 'fill out' but **especially balance** all the areas a bit better. Notice in the chart, which came to look like this second image on the right, that my career and growth areas no longer took all my focus and energy, and the others benefited from more focus and attention.

As my Life Planning work progressed, I was able to say that my Wheel showed greater strengths, but still a good 'filled and rounded' **balance**, among all core areas, as this third Wheel shows.

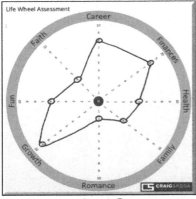

Own Business - No Life Plan

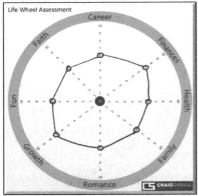

Post Life Plan #1 - Sold Business

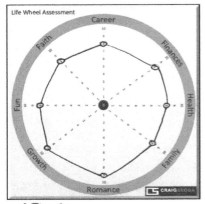

Life Plan #2

Key Learnings — Wheel of Life

What did you learn?

_____
_____
_____
_____
_____
_____
_____

What stood out?

_____
_____
_____
_____
_____

What was a surprise?

_____
_____
_____
_____

What is in question?

_____
_____
_____
_____
_____

CHAPTER 6

LOVE ACCOUNTS:
THE LANGUAGE OF LOVE

"People tend to criticize their spouse most loudly in the area where they themselves have the deepest emotional need."

GARY CHAPMAN

I REALIZE THAT you are doing this Life Planning process as an individual and not as a couple. However, **love** is important. As the song goes, "We're seeking love in all the wrong places." And that, I have found, is because we understand *nothing* about the Languages of Love. Don't think love is not an important topic in any Life Planning and Self-Awareness process!

Love Accounts

Your 'love account' is like your bank account, but it is where you accept deposits of love, approval, affection and appreciation. It is others who make deposits in your love account.

But here is the revealing surprise: It is actually true that the more deposits you make in other people's love accounts, the richer in love and happiness you yourself become! You can make deposits in anyone else's bank account.

But — wait! You also make deposits in your own love account! You do this by doing the opposite of guilt-tripping yourself or beating yourself up about a past mistake or hasty words. Each of us can . . . must . . . love our Self much more.

Do you know what *fills* your love account? What is it that your spouse or friend or even a work relationship like a co-worker <u>does</u> that fills your account up with love and joy, with appreciation and approval? Most of us grow up learning the language of our parents, which was a literal thing or what they actually said coming from their mouth. Their language may not end up being your language . . .

For those in committed relationships: I read a book by Gary Chapman (whom I have quoted on the previous page) called *The Five Love Languages* about 10 years into my marriage. Wow! 10 years too late . . . but better late than never at all. It was a relationship game changer with my wife Tanna. I thought I was doing all the right things to show her I love her. Wrong! I was dead wrong — I was doing the wrong things most of the time, and I did not make nearly enough 'deposits' into Tanna's 'love account' (who jumped in and also did the exercise herself, which is how I now know this . . .).

Ten years of not knowing what your spouse's love language might be is a long time — but a lifetime of not knowing how you yourself expect to experience love, appreciation and approval for yourself is longer. Now that I have awareness of the various languages, I can perceive (it's all about awareness again) how others are expressing love for me . . . another relationship mystery cleared up, that improved how I felt about *myself*.

Find out through this exercise how the people around you really are expressing their feelings. You will never look at people the same way again.

The Languages of Love

The premise of this exercise is we all have a primary love language, something that fills our love account so we consciously and unconsciously know we are loved. There are five main ways we receive and express love. Five languages!! Who knew?

Here they are:

1. **Words of Affirmation** — People with this love language greatly appreciate *hearing spoken* compliments and encouraging words. They feel loved through the positive things they hear. They are pushed away by harsh criticisms.

2. **Quality Time** — People with this love language prefer undivided attention and plenty of *time with* their loved ones. They feel loved when they have lots of time invested in them, but for people with this love language, absence certainly doesn't make the heart grow fonder.

3. **Receiving Gifts** — People with this love language appreciate *receiving presents* and appreciate the thoughts that went into them. They feel loved when they are given gifts spontaneously and are greatly offended when special occasions are forgotten, or a thoughtless gift is given.

4. **Acts of Service (Tasks)** — People with this love language prefer their loved ones to *perform meaningful and thoughtful acts*. It could be as simple as washing the dishes or mowing the lawn, but they appreciate it and feel valued by such deeds. However, they feel unappreciated when they work on a task while their partner just watches without offering to help.

5. **Physical Touch** — People with this love language greatly appreciate *simple physical touching* such as holding hands, hugs or a touch on the arm. It's not just about sex; it's also about knowing that you're there, you are present and nearby, and that you love them. An absence of physical contact has the potential to significantly damage relationships with people who have this love language.

Do you know which language fills your own love account... or that of your spouse... each of your children... your business partner? For many years, I thought my wife's love language was #4, 'tasks and acts of service'. I would do things around the house, fix stuff, go out buy her stuff and so on. After reading the book and discussing the concept of love languages with her, I now know that her love language is #2, 'quality time'. Ho, boy! It really did change our relationship — and how can it not when suddenly you speak the same language together?

Imagine all the people you see daily, such as co-workers, kids, life partner, classmates or roommates. If your respective love accounts are empty from speaking an unknown language to each other, you've got big relationship problems. I dare you to try and get the other person to do something for you if you have neglected to fill his/her love account!

Good luck with that, because when you have a low or zero balance with other people, they are not willing to do anything for you. You 'don't love them', so why should they love you?

If your love account is filled, how sweet life can be! Open your eyes to how others are filling your account, and how they most appreciate their accounts being funded by you. It will get easier as you do it.

Exercise: The Love Languages

Circle the letter of the answer that best applies to you.
This is what **you** like, not what you think your partner wants or likes!

1
A. I like to receive notes of affirmation.
E. I like to be hugged.

2
B. I like to spend one-to-one time with a person who is special to me.
D. I feel loved when someone gives practical help to me.

3
C. I like it when people give me gifts.
B. I like leisurely visits with friends and loved ones.

4
D. I feel loved when people do things to help me.
E. I feel loved when people touch me.

5
E. I feel loved when someone I love or admire puts his or her arm around me.
C. I feel loved when I receive a gift from someone I love or admire.

6
B. I like to go places with friends and loved ones.
E. I like to high-five or hold hands with people who are special to me.

7
C. Visible symbols of love (gifts) are very important to me.
E. I feel loved when people affirm me.

8
E. I like to sit close to people whom I enjoy being around.
A. I like for people to tell me I am beautiful/handsome.

9
B. I like to spend time with friends and loved ones.
C. I like to receive little gifts from friends and loved ones.

10
A. Words of acceptance are important to me.
D. I know someone loves me when he or she helps me.

11
B. I like being together and doing things with friends and loved ones.
A. I like it when kind words are spoken to me.

12
D. What someone does affects me more than what he or she says.
E. Hugs make me feel connected and valued.

13
A. I value praise and try to avoid criticism.
C. Several small gifts mean more to me than one large gift.

14
B. I feel close to someone when we are talking or doing something together.
E. I feel closer to friends and loved ones when they touch me often.

15
A. I like for people to compliment my achievements.
D. I know people love me when they do things for me that they don't enjoy doing.

16
E. I like to be touched as friends and loves ones walk by.
B. I like it when people listen to me and show genuine interest in what I am saying.

17
D. I feel loved when friends and loved ones help me with jobs or projects.
C. I really enjoy receiving gifts from friends and loved ones.

18
A. I like for people to compliment my appearance.
B. I feel loved when people take time to understand my feelings.

19
E. I feel secure when a special person is touching me.
D. Acts of service make me feel loved.

20
D. I appreciate the many things that special people do for me.
C. I like receiving gifts that special people make for me.

21
B. I really enjoy the feeling I get when someone gives me undivided attention.
D. I really enjoy the feeling I get when someone helps me make decisions.

22
C. I feel loved when a person celebrates my birthday with a gift.
A. I feel loved when a person celebrates my birthday with meaningful words.

23
C. I know a person is thinking of me when he or she gives me a gift.
D. I feel loved when a person helps with my chores.

24
B. I appreciate it when someone listens patiently and doesn't interrupt me.
C. I appreciate it when someone remembers special days with a gift.

25
D. I like knowing loved ones are concerned enough to help with my daily tasks.
B. I enjoy extended trips with someone who is special to me.

26
E. I enjoy kissing or being kissed by people with whom I am close.
C. I enjoy receiving a gift given for no special reason.

27
A. I like to be told that I am appreciated.
B. I like for a person to look at me when we are talking.

28
C. Gifts from a friend or loved one are always special to me.
E. I feel good when a friend or loved one touches me.

29
D. I feel loved when a person enthusiastically does some task I have requested.
A. I feel loved when I am told how much I am needed.

30
E. I need to be touched every day.
A. I need words of encouragement daily.

TOTALS: Write the number of times you responded with each <u>letter</u> below.

____ A. Words of Affirmation
____ B. Quality Time
____ C. Receiving Gifts
____ D. Acts of Service
____ E. Physical Touch

The highest number of responses was for _____.
This is my primary language of love!

The second highest number of responses was for _____
_____. This is my secondary language of love!

Use the following chart to make notes about your Primary (#1) and Secondary (#2) languages.

Your Results — Love Languages

Love Language	Description

Key Learnings — Love Languages

What did you learn?

_____

_____

_____

_____

_____

_____

_____

What stood out?

_____

_____

_____

_____

_____

What was a surprise?

_____

_____

_____

_____

_____

What is in question?

_____

_____

_____

_____

_____

CHAPTER 7

TURNING POINTS
AND DECISIONS

*"Life is all about **turning points**. Some people don't embrace them, because they fear change — but over more than 40 years in business, I've learned to see shifts in success and forks in the road as huge opportunities. Turning points, while they often come from moments of darkness, can steer us in the direction of great light . . . or lightbulb moments."*

Sir Richard Branson

HOW DID YOU become who you are?

An important exercise to do to wrap up this introspection on who and how you are is about 'turning points'. Some of how you got to where you are today — became who you have become — originated in past **memorable moments** and **turning points**. These might be your life's major events and experiences of any age, decisions you made or that were made for you, or Ah-Hah moments — any type of occurrence that opened and closed chapters of your life journey or radically changed the direction you had been following, or the beliefs you held as true.

These events were probably a blend of both 'good' and 'bad' memories. They were rarely emotionally neutral, might've often been painful in some way, or full of drama or melodrama.

It is important to draw them up and out of your memory, get them outlined and acknowledge them once again *for the impact they have had on who you are today*, and how you have become the person you now are.

Identifying Turning Points

What is a 'turning point' exactly? It's really just 'something that happens to you' to cause you to make just one change or to start living a new way. Let us look at some descriptions to inspire you to recognize them in your own life.

Examples

- Any of us might consider the death of a parent while we are still young a major life turning point.
- That day at school you chose a musical instrument to learn and how you found out over the course of that first year that you loved and were good at it.
- Your parents' unilateral decision to send you off to a boarding school.
- That week your new teacher discovered you were dyslexic and you started appropriate training . . . finally all the years of suffering you endured from *not* identifying that dyslexia are behind you.
- For a young man's budding interest in food and the food industry, when he enrolled in chef's school on a lark.
- Discovering you have some real talent because it's recognized and identified by someone else.
- For a trained soldier, going overseas into active combat and not being wounded when some of his buddies died — representing an Ah-Hah awakening to other realities in his personal life back home.
- A businessman might remember his big turning point as being refused that bank loan he thought he needed so badly . . . and coming upon some newfound creativity within him to resolve that need differently and successfully.
- When your business was wiped out during the recession, and you cried for a week and were depressed for a month, until . . . (your next Ah-Hah moment came along).

Exercise: Turning Points and Decisions

Here are the steps to doing this exercise of reflection and introspection.

1. Think about the **turning points** in your life, something that affected you or turned your life around, turned it upside down, or moved you into a new direction in a significant way.
2. Write your **age** when it occurred in the age column.
3. Write the turning point, using key phrases to shorten its **description**, but so that you still remember the event. Unless it is obvious, note **+/-** to show that, *at the time it occurred,* you saw the event as positive or negative.
4. Now sit with that memory very, very quietly. Ask yourself, ***"What decision did I make because of that event?"*** (Keep these thoughts for now. You will write them down on page 51.)

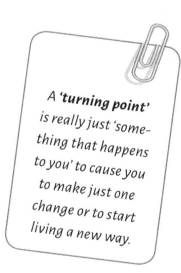

*A '**turning point**' is really just 'something that happens to you' to cause you to make just one change or to start living a new way.*

Write your turning points on the next pages ➜

Turning Point List

Age	Turning Point Specifics +/-	Description

Turning Point List

Age	Turning Point Specifics +/-	Description

Now that you have identified your turning points and reflected on the personal decision each one led you to make, there is one next thing to do.

Experts in therapy and in Emotional Intelligence agree: Whatever the **decision** we made at the time, we did it to:

- **protect ourselves or others and keep ourselves safe**
- **defend our best interests as we defined them at the time**

Those experts also agree:

> *Such decisions made in the past might just be what is*
> *sabotaging our present success, happiness and fulfillment.*

Reflect on <u>how</u> those past decisions have played out over time. How have they affected your life in each core area of the Life Wheel? How have they made you behave? How have they colored your interactions with others? How have they opened or closed your mind and heart? Are these decisions still your 'friends' or have they become 'enemies' to your growth?

Beware! The same circumstances, occurring for 2 different people, will result in 2 different decisions.

Examples:

Turning point was death of both parents at age 7 and being fostered with a much older (grandma-aged) aunt.
- Decision of Individual #1: "I am always loved and cared for."
- Decision of Individual #2: "I will always be abandoned by people I love in my life, so I mustn't get attached to anyone."

Do you see how a similar event can lead two people to take opposite decisions? Can you sit a minute and imagine how life played out for each person over the next 30 years, and how that old decision colors actions they have taken? The **ramifications** are very different!

Exercise: Decisions & Ramifications

Decisions List

Decision you made:	How it has materialized or played out over time:	Do you still believe this decision should direct your life in any way, yes or no?

Decisions List

Decision you made:	How it has materialized or played out over time:	Do you still believe this decision should direct your life in any way, yes or no?

Exercise: Turning Points and Core Domains

Lastly, you assign your **turning points** to one or more Life Wheel domains. Use the grid below to sort your turning points. This will help you see how many and which turning points you have had in each domain ... or that you have had none in some domains.

TO BEGIN: Choose the 5 turning points that still stir up emotions in you — positively or negatively — and write them in the following chart in the middle column. (HINT: If you got emotional remembering or writing it out, that qualifies as an important turning point to pay attention to!)

1. Choose the five turning points.
2. Write in your age at the time of each one.
3. Fill in which core domain — one or more of them — was impacted by that event. If you notice that not all 8 of the core domains are on your list, that is just fine.

Turning Points Summary

AGE	SPECIFICS	LIFE DOMAIN(S)

When you are done with this task, see if you notice any *themes* that group your turning points and/or decisions together.

Key Learnings — Turning Points & Past Decisions

What did you learn?

_____

_____

_____

_____

_____

_____

What stood out?

_____

_____

_____

_____

What was a surprise?

_____

_____

_____

_____

What is in question?

_____

_____

_____

_____

CHAPTER 8

QUESTIONING
THE COMFORT ZONE

*"When you stop expecting people to be perfect,
you can like them for who they are."*

DONALD MILLER

AS YOU REVIEW all of the exercises, assessments and thinking you have done individually in this Part 1, you may have noticed that they bring into question that 'space' we all call our **comfort zone**.

We come to the subject of our personal tendencies and habits, since they are part of the building blocks that helped us construct that comfort zone. A 'tendency' is a natural predisposition to do something in a given way, which you saw in the DISC assessment, or to speak in a certain manner, which you might've noticed from the Love Language exercise. A 'habit' is something you routinely do or a way you predictably say things as a matter of course, which you see in your morning routine at home or the way you typically end your day after work or play.

Experts believe that about 70% of all our actions on any given day are habitual. We don't think about them very much, if at all. And we certainly don't question the rightness or wrongness, the benefits or the drawbacks of doing that thing.

The exercises I have provided for you here in Part 1 have hopefully allowed you to pay more attention to your habits and tendencies and question them at least a little bit.

Experts believe that about 70% of all our actions on any given day are habitual.

Awareness, Again

When I did these exercises, some of my tendencies and habits that I hadn't paid too much attention to in the past popped out and came more fully into my awareness. Because they entered my awareness, I could analyze them and make some decisions. You can't do anything about a habit or tendency unless you are aware of it in the first place. Awareness is really your starting point.

Exercise:

Go to the following four charts. You are going to group all your 'Key Learnings' charts in which you answered 4 questions and put them together.

- In point #1, about what you learned, write all those answers (or the key words) together in the first chart.
- Then look at point #2, about what stood out for you, and write them out one after another in the next chart.
- For #3, about surprises you had, group all those comments in a third chart.
- For #4, about what is still in question, do the same thing.

Do you see any patterns in those comments or responses? Key words or phrases that are repeated? For instance, in every surprise chart, have you written something like, "I never realized that about myself"? Look for such patterns now. Circle them. Think about them some more.

1. All "What did you learn?" responses:

2. All "What stood out?" responses:

3. All "What was a surprise?" responses:

4. All "What is in question?" responses:

Expectations

Our tendencies and habits are apparent in our usual and adaptive behaviors which you have started to discover through the DISC assessment. Our DISC behavioral style — along with all our education, life experiences, habits and tendencies — shows us how we all have *expectations*. Expectations are also born out of our family or cultural traditions. We have expectations about:

- How others should speak — Speak quietly indoors; don't criticize people to their face
- How to respond and behave — Be respectful to the boss; don't run or shout in the library
- What other people's roles need to be — Dad takes the trash out; mom does the grocery shopping and cooking; the kids do their own laundry
- And what should happen when and how — We need our annual family birthday celebrations and wedding anniversary special gifts . . . or the world will explode

We base our expectations of others on what we ourselves would do, no secret there. Donald Miller might well have said, "If you stop expecting people to be *just like you*, you can finally see them for the person they have always been" . . . and start enjoying their company!

This said, improving any relationship or making a single 'radical' change or determined change in direction as you might be by embarking on this Life Planning process, will require you to move away from your natural expectations, habits and tendencies (if only momentarily) and open up more than might be comfortable at first.

Open Your Mind Up

One of my friends told me that the French have a saying about 'provincial thinking' — when they accuse themselves or someone else of 'provincial thinking', it means they have been behaving in a <u>small-minded</u> way. Here in the US, we'd call this *small-town thinking*.

Exercise:

This is an exercise I learned from a Navy Seal. Do this now:

→ Stand up

→ Put one arm out horizontally in front of you

→ Close your eyes, turn to the right (or left, as you wish) and try to point your arm behind your back and even beyond, going as far as you comfortably can

→ Visually mark where your arm was pointing when you reached as far as you could

→ Now turn back to the front

→ Now picture an owl and how it can turn its head all the way around

→ Now do the exercise again and push yourself and extra 25%, visually noting where you stopped

→ How much further did you stretch? (Usually it is 25 to 50%)

We limit our thinking in the same automated way we stretched our arm around behind us the *first* time. The challenge is that we don't learn how to stretch our thinking the second and next times!

As you examine how you became what you are today as well as where you wish to take yourself and who you wish to become, there will be a lot of 'mind blowing' or mind-expanding moments. Embrace them and enjoy the journey!

Expectations, habits and routines keep us in a box. Like a horse with blinders on, you cannot see the infinite possibilities available to you because you cannot see far enough around you and out onto the horizon. So we settle. In settling, we create a small impenetrable, unshakable comfortable zone around ourselves. Most of the time, we never step outside that zone. We don't peek outside the blinders and never even think to tear them off! We complacently play the cards we were dealt and live inside a box — with a hand of cards and a box of our own creation. Saying, "This is how I am, so I cannot improve . . . earn more . . . be happier . . . " is a cop out!

Don't Settle!

Embarking on creating a Life Plan is a statement about your desire to shake off that complacency, to step outside that comfort zone, and question 'how things are right now' as opposed to 'how things could be'. Living intentionally is about setting your sights on living in a bigger way.

Exercise:

Look back at all your responses in the **Turning Point** exercise. As you review those memorable moments, events and Ah-Ha realizations, ask yourself if any of them occurred because you had blinders on — because you'd <u>settled</u> in to a 'clueless' or limited state of mind. My guess is that at least one painful or unpleasant thing happened to you because you were in your comfort zone, with blinders on.

You were, quite literally, blindsided. How you reacted to it or acted because of it also probably arose from your habits and routines, so see if that's the case right now as you reflect on it.

This exercise is not by any means to make you feel bad or make you wrong. You acted and reacted with the tools you had and did the best you could. My point? Lots of unpleasant things can happen to us because we have settled into our comfort zone. We've kept our mind closed to other potentiality.

See that you were closed off; commit to opening up . . . if only just a little at a time.

CHAPTER 9

WHERE ARE YOU NOW?

TAKE A FEW days if you think you need them to let all the preceding personal and introspective exercises settle. Then, pick up a pen and write your personal answers to these questions:

1. How would you describe the place and space you are in right now in your life as a whole? Try to write a few sentences about this.

2. How would you describe the place and space you are in right now in each of the core domains? Try to write at least one sentence for each of the 8 core domains. (You might end up describing how some domains are not working for you and if you have ideas at this point for change, and write about the ways the others are going well and how you still might make improvements or changes.)

Fun:

Faith:

Finances:

Family:

Career:

Health:

Growth:

Romance:

3. Would you be happy to stay in this place and space forever, until the end of your natural days, yes or no? Why or why not? Try to write a few sentences about this.

4. On a scale of **0 to 10**, with 0 being no will or ability and 10 being a strong will or ability:

_____ **a.** How willing and able are you to make gentle changes in your *personal* habits, tendencies and routines? Write which habits, tendencies and routines those are.

_____**b.** How willing and able are you to learn something new about an area that is already one of your 'strengths'? Why? What? Name the strength(s). Try to write a few sentences about this.

_____ **c.** How willing and able are you to correct the language of love you have been 'speaking' (in the case you have 'had it all wrong' up till now)? State some ways you can make such changes.

5. What goal(s) would you personally like to achieve that you have not yet given much time to? The goals can be in any of the core domains — or you might set a goal in each one of them. (HINT: We'll do much more on this later, but just get the best start you can right now.)

6. What family goals have come to mind as you have done this introspective self-discovery work? Name them all! And then? Share them with whoever is involved (your parents, spouse or children).

PART 2

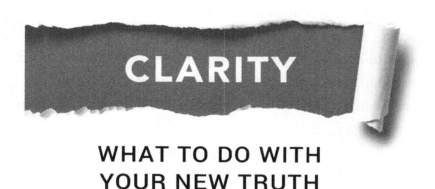

CLARITY

WHAT TO DO WITH YOUR NEW TRUTH

*"There are few things more powerful
than a life lived with passionate clarity."*

ERWIN MCMANUS

TO RECAP WHERE you should be in this journey, you should:

→ Have identified your 5 natural strengths
→ Know your one or two strongest DISC behavior styles
→ Understand your Emotional Intelligence Quotient or EQ
→ Know your primary love language
→ Have drawn your core domains wheel and know how healthy
   (round/flat) your Life Wheel is
→ Have let all the above information and responses settle

Back to Awareness

Clarity is like brand-new knowledge, isn't it? I know it has energized me! It takes a while to take it all in, connect the dots from the stuff you already knew about yourself to the new stuff. It takes time to admit that your mind and perspective have opened up . . . and then to keep it open. It's called 'processing'. And it's all about greater awareness or consciousness about yourself.

You've gotten some new perspective on yourself. You have taken some time to absorb this new knowledge about yourself. I have to say you will probably have discovered some blend of awareness and blindness about yourself. Perhaps you have long since developed a clear awareness of who and how you are — but only in some of your facets. I'm guessing that in many cases, however, your eyes will be opened to a new aspect of yourself! Embrace all the revelations! You might have to come to grips with the surprises you had, which might include:

- Getting used to having/speaking a love language you never identified before
- Having your behavior style so clearly mapped out for you by the DISC exercise
- Seeing your Emotional Intelligence — or lack of it — starkly presented to you
- Nodding in understanding of your core strengths, finally revealed in so many key words
- Putting the areas of your life that haven't been working in a brand-new light (flat . . . round) through the Wheel of Life

Awareness — this clarity — is your starting point. It is new or restated (even rediscovered) knowledge. In this Part 2 of our book, I will be helping you, through more exercises, to **_expand and deepen your clarity._**

CHAPTER 10

TIME, OR EMPOWERING YOURSELF 24/7/365

YOU DON'T HAVE more power just yet, but you do have more knowledge.

What are you going to do with this knowledge now?

The real power of all knowledge comes in taking action on it.

A life plan is one way to take action. Setting specific goals to change in different areas you have been identifying as 'needing help' is another.

In order to take action, many of us need to carve out the *time* to do so. *Time* for reflection on a direction, a goal, a change. *Time* to implement or do what we have decided. Let's look as a start at how you are spending your precious *time* right now.

Time is our only non-renewable resource.

Note: If you are thinking that 'this time thing' is not such an important matter to deal with, consider this:

Time is our only non-renewable resource.

Waste your *time* if you wish, but you will never get it back again.

Exercise: Daily Time Usage Assessment

Use the following chart and the *daily* activities I have listed as your start to calculating how you currently spend your time. Customize it by writing in the activities you do that I have not put on this list.

Note how long you spend at the activity and how you judge that usage of the time. How does this look? I show you 3 examples below:

Example:

Morning grooming	35 minutes	**Well spent** [your reasoning — "I felt ready for anything!"]
Breakfast	10 minutes	**Wasted** [your reasoning — "It was just coffee, not a 'breakfast of champions' "]
Conversation with family	10 minutes	**Wasted** [your reasoning — "We got a bit irritated with each other; not very loving!"]

Daily Time Usage Assessment

Activity:	Time Spent Today:	Well Spent / Wasted?
Morning grooming to start the day		
Breakfast		
Conversation with family — after work/school		
Commute — morning (include all travel time if don't work in one place all day)		
Computer — work related only (include email, agenda, reports, document creation, etc.)		
Work related meetings — whole day (include pre- and post-chatting and organization activities)		
Lunch		
Computer — at work, personal only		
Smoking — at work		
Drinking — at work		
Downtime chatting — at work		
Sitting/standing at work doing no work		
Commute — afternoon/end of work day (include all travel time if don't work in one place all day)		
Dinner — restaurant / Bar or Club — evening		
Television — news, reality shows, sitcoms, etc.		
YouTube viewing and surfing		
Movies		

Daily Time Usage Assessment (cont.)

Activity:	Time Spent Today:	Well Spent / Wasted?
Social media reading, posting, surfing		
Web surfing for 'window shopping'		
Laughter		
Conversation with family — after work/school		
Time with Spouse/Partner immediately after work		
Cooking at home — alone or with family members, friends		

Daily Time Usage Assessment (cont.)

Activity:	Time Spent Today:	Well Spent / Wasted?

Judgment Call

Look again at the activities you have stated were **time well spent**. Would you say that they were *important* activities (work or job related, for example) — with some of those important activities also being *urgent* (time sensitive and need to be done now)? Also ask yourself if activities you marked as time well spent were *not really* very important or at all urgent.

Look now at the activities you stated as **time wasted**. Was it time wasted because you were waiting for something to happen, procrastinating or spinning your wheels? Was it time wasted because you needed to re-do some poorly executed task? Was it time wasted because you embarked on the activity with too few facts or information to bring it to a successful conclusion? Or, as in surfing the Internet (blog-reading, social media, YouTube viewing, and so on), watching TV, sitting down at the corner bar for an extended Happy Hour — was the time wasted as your excuse for 'relaxation'?

This is all a judgment call — very subjective. But it is your judgment that counts.

Exercise: Time Management Assessment

You've just looked at how you <u>spend</u> your time. Through the 15 questions of this fast online time management quiz, you can look at how you manage your time. Managing your time is about choices you make and, according to this expert source, comes from *goal setting* (or not), *prioritizing* tasks you do on a daily basis (or not prioritizing at all), from knowing how to manage *interruptions* effectively (or getting waylaid every time you are interrupted), and knowing if/when you *procrastinate* (or jump right in to things).

Time Management Assessment

Instructions

1. Go online to:
   https://www.mindtools.com/pages/article/newHTE_88.htm
2. Answer the 15 questions and click 'Calculate my Total'
3. Read the assessment of your scores in the sections below the questionnaire.
4. Record it all in the box below.

Time Management and Me:

You may ask how writing out how we spend/manage our time empowers us. To apply your new knowledge and to create and implement a Life Plan, you might well need to carve out time that you cannot yet see in your schedule. So many individuals, not to mention couples and families, seem to be busy every minute of the day. But as you have probably seen from the two exercises you just did:

1. You probably don't grant yourself regularly scheduled downtime as an individual or in family
2. You probably waste more time than you imagined or at least use it in ways that don't 'move you forward'

You may need to reprioritize (manage it through new choices) some of the ways you are using your time today, and later we will see how. You cannot do that unless you know how you are spending your time now. Once again, awareness leads to knowledge which can empower you as you take action.

Example: One of my clients had a new priority (see more on those later) for herself, and decided to eliminate, 'cold turkey', all evenings spent outside the home, no matter whose company (work colleagues or personal friends) was involved. Evenings were henceforth spent in a new way: focusing on that new priority and goal of hers.

Though you may not be able to do what she did, you will find a need to eliminate at least some of your time wasters in order to carve out time for your priority of working your Life Plan and those action items. Creating more time by getting up earlier or going to bed later is another way of managing your time.

Here is another way to view this issue: When you say Yes to something, you are intentionally saying No to something else. Example: If I say Yes to having a drink after work with a friend, I am knowingly saying No to being on time for dinner at home with my wife.

Key Learnings — Time Usage & Time Management

What did you learn?

_____

_____

_____

_____

_____

_____

What stood out?

_____

_____

_____

_____

_____

What was a surprise?

_____

_____

_____

_____

_____

What is in question?

_____

_____

_____

_____

_____

CHAPTER 11

VALUES:
WHAT YOU BELIEVE

"You are living someone else's life
if you don't know what you believe in and why."

IF SOMEONE WERE to ask you, "What do you stand for?", what would you respond?

This question is about what you believe. It is not a matter of politics, as many might think! What you stand for is simply your beliefs and what is important to you — on a personal basis, in your life and relationships with others, and out in the world. We call those important things our **'core values'**.

Have you sat down and truly defined what is important to you? That not only takes time, but willingness to go deep into your heart and soul. In order to live on purpose, intentionally, and support what is important to you, these are definitions that need to be made. You make them by digging down deep inside of yourself.

I see people every day who have never articulated their *core, or primary, values*, never really given thought to what they stand for as an individual (much less as a couple or family). I really want to help those people get clarity on their values! Without knowing your core values and what you stand for, you will be in a state of unhappy confusion (and potentially chaos) that revisits you time and again over the years.

You know the story about the house built on sand. That house does not stand very long; it tumbles into a ruin. It cannot provide shelter for its inhabitants, who are thus lost in the world without a home. Your core values are like the foundation that your house — your home — is built on. When your values disintegrate, every-thing around you disintegrates, because you and your actions are not in harmony with your beliefs or core values. ***However, core values keep you somewhat flexible while moving in the right direction, just like the banks of a river.*** The river (your path through life) is never straight — and the banks (your core values) keep you moving in the right direction.

Take a step back and simply answer this question:

Do I know what I will absolutely say YES or NO to?

If not — and that is normal — it is time to define your core values!

One important fact to keep in mind about **values** as you get into a *process* of identifying, clarifying, and writing down your core values: It is not a single event, but an ongoing process. You do not do this one-time-and-done. Your core values shouldn't change much over time, though your purpose may — and that is fine. Never forget about it; it is a dynamic progression.

From Core Domains to Core Values

'Core' domains — those eight key areas our lives could be divided into for our attention — are already familiar to you. I used them in your **Wheel of Life** (chapter 5), where they are the key concept, and where they name the segments of the wheel.

I like to say that our *values* really either *affect or originate* from each of these domains of our life.

The core domains I said that I see in us all — and which you incorporate into your Life Plan as a minimum number of domains — are:

1. **Personal Growth** (Self-improvement, including Education)
2. **Family** (Close or Extended)
3. **Career** (Job, Vocation)
4. **Faith** (Spirituality)

We each come to life with a different mindset. Yet all of us deal with life from these domains. Let's chew on that some more, and circle back to our work in the previous chapter on *Time*:

---

1. Are you playing an infinite or finite game of life?

   a. Finite games have a definite beginning and ending. There are rules, with the game ending by someone needing to be winning.
   b. Infinite games do not have a beginning or ending. They are viewed as a game of continual play and sometimes new players come into the game. There is no talk of winners or losers.

2. Do you live as if your days are numbered?

   a. When you plan out your days, weeks, years, do you have the attitude that you have a specific number of days left here on earth?
   b. Do you prioritize appropriate tasks as though your days are numbered?

Defining your core values is a hard thing to do. You probably rarely speak them out loud in so many words. They are deep inside of you and you may not have the words to easily describe them. In order to get your mind ready for the one action item below which is to define your core values, work through your thoughts around the above questions. We really do approach life from a 'marriage' of time and values.

Go now to the exercise on the next page, the **Warm Up**. It is a simple matter of answering each question as fully as you can.

Exercise: Core Values Warm-up

Core Values Warm Up Exercise Questions

1. What are my life roles? *(Examples: parent, spouse/committed life partner, manager, coach, brother, sister, son, daughter, manager, employer, etc.)*

2. What people, things, or activities seem most important to me?

3. When I don't have pressure in my life, what do I like to do?

4. If I knew I only had 90 days to live, what would I do with that time?

5. When my life is over:

   a. What will I be glad I did?

   b. What would I like my obituary to say about me?

   c. What would I like others to remember about me?

6. What do I really do well?

7. Is there something I feel I should do but haven't ever had the courage to do?

Let's now identify your core values. The following Core Values Worksheet will help you put your values to paper.

Exercise: Core Values Worksheet

Note that it is very important in the second column to answer both questions for each role: the 'what' is important and the 'why' is equally important. You should ask and answer the 'why' with 3-5 responses for each role.

1. List your **roles** from the Core Values Warm Up Exercise (question #1) in the left-side roles column of the charts on the next pages.
2. In the center column:
    *   Write **what** is important to you about this role.
    *   Write **why** this is important to you.
    *   Each of these two statements may be several sentences. Write everything that comes to mind.
    *   Repeat this process for all your roles.
3. We go now to that right-side column, where your value statement is written. Start back at the top of your list and determine if there are common words or themes in your **what** and **why** statements that allow you to formulate a couple of **core value <u>statements</u>**. (You do not have to have a core value for each role, because your foundation may cover multiple areas or roles in your life.)
    *   Bring each statement down to a concise sentence or phrase.
4. Now the fun part—you have to test your values.
    *   Identify situations where your core values can potentially hurt you.
    *   **Example**: Having a core value of 'innovation' when you thrive on 'stability' (and *not* constant change) is contradictory. Thus, a core value called 'innovation' will not make it to the top of your list. However, if you can't think of a case where the named value steers you wrong, you probably have a keeper, so put an * near that one.
5. Validate your core values with a trusted friend by asking if he/she thinks of that value when thinking of you.
    *   Remember, they are your core values. Be careful not to make someone else's thoughts become yours. This is your life.

Core Values Worksheet

Role	What's important about this role? <u>Why</u>?	Core Value

Core Values Worksheet (cont.)

Role	What's important about this role? Why?	Core Value

Values and Behaviors

Now it is time to identify those asterisked values — the ones that are keepers — and look at each one more closely. Write each of those core values in the 'Core Value' space on the table on the next pages. You probably have at least five, but however many there are — include them. Next, you look for how that named value/belief plays out in your life and in your behaviors.

Example: If **'compassion for all'** is one of your values, list it in the chart. Then, in the box below that, try to name some *specific visible personal behaviors* of yours that <u>illustrate</u> this core value or belief to anyone watching you. Keep it simple! It could be as simple as

- "listening to a panhandler instead of just walking by"
- "giving everyone the benefit of the doubt until I have a full picture"

Go ahead and do that now with the values you have retained.

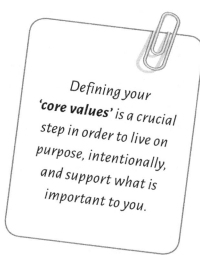

Defining your 'core values' is a crucial step in order to live on purpose, intentionally, and support what is important to you.

Continue on the next pages ➜

Core Values and Behaviors Worksheet

Core Value

Specific, Observable Behaviors that Demonstrate Your Core Value and Belief

Core Value

Specific, Observable Behaviors that Demonstrate Your Core Value and Belief

Core Value

Specific, Observable Behaviors that Demonstrate Your Core Value and Belief

Core Value

Specific, Observable Behaviors that Demonstrate Your Core Value and Belief

Core Values and Behaviors Worksheet (cont.)

Core Value

Specific, Observable Behaviors that Demonstrate Your Core Value and Belief

Core Value

Specific, Observable Behaviors that Demonstrate Your Core Value and Belief

Core Value

Specific, Observable Behaviors that Demonstrate Your Core Value and Belief

Core Value

Specific, Observable Behaviors that Demonstrate Your Core Value and Belief

Your Key Learnings — Core Values & Beliefs

What did you learn?

_____

_____

_____

_____

_____

_____

What stood out?

_____

_____

_____

_____

_____

What was a surprise?

_____

_____

_____

_____

What is in question?

_____

_____

_____

_____

_____

CHAPTER 12

YOUR PERSONAL MISSION:
KNOW YOUR WHY OR LOSE YOUR WAY

"We don't invent our missions, we detect them."

STEPHEN COVEY

HAVE YOU EVER watched an individual determinedly storm around in a whirlwind, speak on the phone with great authority and purpose, or dynamically lead other people to get something urgent done — and *right now*!? We typically say about such a person that he is '*on a mission*'!

To become further empowered, you will find it necessary to know your 'why' or your 'mission'. You can call it 'my mission in life', or 'my personal mission'. You can call it 'my raison d'être' or just 'my Why'. Just as any business and charitable organization knows which mission they are on and writes out their organization's Mission Statement for all to see, so should you.

Your Mission is why you wake up excited in the morning!

A Personal Mission Statement is a brief description of what you want to focus on, what you want to accomplish, and what you want to become. It is not like a goal, in the sense that it won't be something you 'do', per se. It is more the direction you are taking yourself. It allows you to focus your energy, actions, behaviors and decisions towards the things that are most important to you. The written statement creates a picture in your mind. It directs your life, your career, your family and what you personally want to accomplish. Your mission statement can be a two- or three-word statement or a full page — as long as it defines what your mission is.

Features of a personal mission statement:
- Characterizes the deepest and best within you
- Provides value to others with a purpose of contribution
- Utilizes your unique strengths and gifts
- Addresses all the significant roles in your life
- Applies to all spokes of your Life Wheel
- Is bigger than yourself yet feels totally right for you
- Is based on the principle of producing quality-of-life results (not standards of living)
- It is written to inspire <u>you</u>, regardless of what others say or think

Your Personal Mission Statement can make a major difference in your life. We all have anything from 'a vague idea' to a 'clear-cut vision' of where we are going, but when you pair up a Mission Statement with your core values and clarity about who and how you are (from all the exercises we've done together so far), you have clearly articulated where you are going and why. The 'how' almost magically takes care of itself. A mission of clarity brings focus and purpose to your life.

Your Personal Mission Statement is a powerful tool because it provides you with a path for success, and it gives you permission to say 'No' to the things that are distractions.

WARNING: Your mission will change over time! As we get older, we have more life experiences and acquire new skills. If your Mission Statement doesn't change, you run the risk of it not being relevant to you some years down the road.

What does a Mission Statement look like? Here are some examples of such statements (all 'short and sweet', as you can see) to inspire you.

- Bring beauty into people's lives.
- Contribute to society.
- Raise a great family that understands giving.
- Make a difference.
- Have peace.

- Create joy.
- Excel in my field.
- Help others move from success to significance.

My own Mission Statement is: "Help people be better than they thought they could be."

Exercise: Your Personal Mission Statement

You will be writing out a number of versions of your Personal Mission Statement until you feel comfortable owning one of them. It needs to support who you are, who you want to be, and what you want to accomplish. Make sure you allocate enough time to get this right.

1. Follow Steps 1-5 on the following Mission Statement Worksheet.
2. Reflect on the 2 questions in Step 6.
3. Start working on your Personal Mission Statement by creating 3-10 different ones. They may just be 'versions' of each other, or entirely different from the others. Up to you.
4. Select the one that fits you best . . . for today, right now.

Mission Statement Worksheet

Step 1 - List your 5 Strengths (from Strengths Finders Assessment, in Part 1)

Step 2 - List your primary DISC style; write the top 5-10 words that describe those typical behaviors

Step 3 - List your most notable skills, talents and abilities (music, teaching, planning, etc.)

Step 4 - List your core values (from previous chapter)

Step 5 - List your dreams and passions (as if money is no object)

Step 6 - Write a number of versions of your Personal Mission Statement

Now write the one or two versions of the Personal Mission Statement that feel right to you.

My Personal Mission Statement

Key Learnings — Your Personal Mission Statement

What did you learn?

_____

_____

_____

_____

_____

_____

What stood out?

_____

_____

_____

_____

What was a surprise?

_____

_____

_____

_____

What is in question?

_____

_____

_____

_____

_____

CHAPTER 13

THE WHEEL OF LIFE, AGAIN

IT'S TIME TO return to the Wheel of Life that you drew in Part 1. You might remember with some humiliation that your wheel was not full of air, but flat on one or more sides! I can empathize! You saw my Wheels!

The good news is that it can be corrected. Doing just that is what is next, through four specific questions for each domain.

Here are the four questions, and you ask them about each of those 8 domains (however full or flat they now are):

1. What's **<u>right</u>** about this domain called . . . ?
2. What's **<u>wrong</u>** about this domain called . . . ?
3. What is **<u>confusing</u>** about this domain called . . . ?
4. What is **<u>missing</u>** from this domain called . . . ?

The flatter any domain is, the longer your answers will be with each of the questions 2, 3 and 4. The fuller the domain is, the longer (perhaps) your answers to question 1 will be.

Examples:

1. What's **<u>right</u>** about this domain called Romance?
    - We spend 3 nights a week together without the kids.

2. What's **<u>wrong</u>** about this domain called Health?
    - I overeat processed/cooked food even though it disagrees with my digestion.

3. What is **<u>confusing</u>** about this domain called Faith/Spirituality?
    - I haven't found a way to 'access' the quietness, and prayer-time doesn't seem to be the solution.

4. What is **<u>missing</u>** from this domain called Career?
    - A way to earn more: I've been settling for less pay than I know I'm worth.

Exercise: Wheel of Life Clarity

1. What's **<u>right</u>** about this domain called . . . ?

Career

Finances

Health

Family

Romance

Growth

Fun

Faith

2. What's <u>**wrong**</u> about this domain called . . . ?

Career

Finances

Health

Family

Romance

Growth

Fun

Faith

3. What's **<u>confusing</u>** about this domain called . . . ?

Career

Finances

Health

Family

Romance

Growth

Fun

Faith

4. What's **<u>missing</u>** from this domain called . . . ?

Career

Finances

Health

Family

Romance

Growth

Fun

Faith

CHAPTER 14

LEGACY QUESTIONS

"One day you will wake up and there won't be any more time to do the things you've always wanted. Do it now."

PAULO COELHO

THIS STATEMENT BY Paulo only drives home to us that 'time is our only non-renewable resource' and we need to treat it like the valuable treasure it is. That is why I always ask life planning clients to study how they use and manage their time!

There are a lot of regrets people have when they look back on their life and how they spent it. They are variously expressed, according to which organization has done the survey, but they boil down for almost everyone to these (presented in no particular order from several survey results I have read):

1. <u>Didn't have enough fun:</u> I wish I had been happier, worried less and enjoyed life more.
2. <u>Worked too much:</u> I wish I had chosen work that was meaningful for me. I wish I had not spent so much time working and away from those I love and who loved me.
3. <u>Didn't have the courage to do what I wanted to do and did what everyone else told me to do</u> **(which is the #1 regret across all surveys!)**: I wish I had not listened to the fear so often. I wish I had taken more risks. I wish I had lived my own dream.
4. <u>Didn't take care of myself:</u> I wish I had eaten better, exercised more, created more physical energy for myself. I wish I'd taken care of my health and wellness more intelligently.

5. <u>Didn't love or express love enough:</u> I wish I had been a better spouse (parent, child, friend). I wish I had been more loving to the people who mattered the most. I wish hadn't been so afraid to say, "I love you" or even "How've you been?" more often.

6. <u>Worried too much about money:</u> I wish I had not fretted because, looking back, I had it all. I wish I hadn't said 'can't afford it' as often as I did, because it wasn't true!

Some of our regrets are about what we call the **Opus Gloria**: Our life's *work* (Opus) or foremost lifetime *contribution* (glory to God or Gloria) that we are remembered for. It is the legacy we leave when we are gone. Ego gets in the way more often than anyone likes to admit. We didn't give, because, "Hey, I've got a family to provide for." Or we were afraid our talents or contribution would somehow be seen as too little or not good enough — and we know we avoid such blows to our Ego, right?

Legacy can also refer to how we want our friends, family and close colleagues to speak of us at our funeral — how will their separate eulogies sound? What will you have given them to say?

Correcting things before you get to that sad point of regret begins now.

Life is finite and, as they say, 'tomorrow never comes', so taking the time to prioritize, doing the things that are important to you now, listening better, telling people you love and appreciate them . . . **must start now**.

To get to the bottom of regrets and nip them in the bud, I invite you to ponder several more important questions that will help. Instead of dwelling on potential regrets, take a more positive, proactive approach and call them the **Legacy Questions**.

Exercise: Legacy Questions

1. Consider the questions in the next chart.
2. You may have several answers at this point to each question. Write all your answers in the next table.

Legacy Questions

What is the single thing you want to be remembered for?

What is the most important legacy to leave to your family, friends, and colleagues?

What do you care about that you must no longer ignore or must take action on?

What childhood or current dream(s) of yours are you not acting on?

What would you like eulogies about you to say by speakers at your own funeral — if you could change your life now to make them true?

The plan we'll be creating starting in Part 3 joins your head and your heart. It joins the facts of your life today to the new realities you are in the process of creating for tomorrow. If you do this planning and all the preceding exercises with your heart and head connected, you will create a Life Plan that will bring you clarity and peace about your quality of life and living now and your future.

Your future is your legacy. You start building that today, and your Life Plan is the foundation and the structure that you build your legacy upon.

Have you ever thought ahead 50 or 100 years? I have a friend who does that regularly in a specific way. She's a meditator (which she insists is not necessary to do this) and sits in her quietness and pictures herself as a 99-year-old. She has a whole imagery around this, and ends up by having her 99-year-old-self turn around to face her current self with advice. She just sits and listens. She says it is always a comforting exercise in 'getting her priorities straight again'.

Exercise: A New Slant on Time

Legacy thinking starts today. I was recently asked the questions you see in the box below. Answer them for yourself right now.

1. If you knew without a shadow of doubt that you'd live until age 102 (brain and body intact!), how would your actions and behaviors and attitudes of today change?

2. Would you set bigger or different or more goals? Write a few thoughts about this.

3. Would your Personal Mission or Core Values be different? How? Write a few thoughts about this.

These questions boggled my mind, actually stunned me for long moment! My mind surely opened by the mental vision of 'knowing we'll live to 102'. I woke up to new life potential:

I had a light-bulb moment that my goals were not big enough. Surely, if what you are doing right now feels right, that is the right thing to be doing — and I am. But . . . I'd want what I'm doing to 'be bigger' if I lived to 102!

My great Big Hairy Audacious Goal didn't seem so huge put in that context . . . living as many more decades as I'd already lived? Wow! My goals were suddenly not nearly far-reaching enough when I thought about living to 102.

I started seeing (with more time — decades! — available) how much more I could achieve, not only in my coaching business with the bigger audiences I could reach, but how I could be out in the greater society making more of a difference, too.

An envisioned future and image of self are parts of this. A purposeful ripple effect sets in which is where your passions and strengths intersect. You know who you are, so you head off to your job and spend the day in a sweet (happy) spot at work. When you are in your sweet spot (happy) at work, you also go home happy, you positively impact your family. Your image of yourself and your sweet life is a ripple impacting the people around you and the world you live in. This rippling effect continues through the days, weeks, months and years — creating good feelings and experiences all week long for you and others.

Legacy thinking starts today, and sets you up to be in such a sweet spot all the time. A legacy is not so much in leaving money or other tangible assets when you die, as we too often think. It can be that if you wish, but it can also be so much more than that! It is about how you had a hand in positively changing others or an aspect of the world at large, or about your contributions to others in real time (not tomorrow, but now).

Your Key Learnings — Legacy

What did you learn?

_____

_____

_____

_____

_____

_____

What stood out?

_____

_____

_____

_____

_____

What was a surprise?

_____

_____

_____

_____

_____

What is in question?

_____

_____

_____

_____

_____

CHAPTER 15

YOUR ONE GUIDING
WORD & TRIGGERS

All words have energy and power.

WORDS HAVE SUCH tremendous power, to hurt or to heal. We are reminded of the childhood chant about 'sticks and stones' that state 'but words will never hurt me!' Not so true! But as parents and teachers, we did our best to train our kids to think for themselves instead of believing every word others throw at them.

Words also have their own energy, which we don't consider often enough. Here is an illustration:

- When your toddler is joyful, but not saying a word — how do you <u>know</u> he is happy?
- When a store clerk is grumpy, but nonetheless has a customer-first smile on her face — how do you <u>know</u> he's grumpy?

It's in the **energy** each one projects outward! We capture that energy and it is a very real part of our human communication.

I have found that just by observing people for a little while I can often choose one word that describes their life's actions and strategy.

There is a very popular young fellow on the YouTube circuit named Evan Carmichael whose mission is to help people grow and succeed (and in case you have thought I'm crazy about personal missions, this fellow tells his audience his mission in every single video!). He encourages his followers to find their '**One Word**', which he defines as a positive guiding force in our everyday living. His is 'Believe'.

Example:

One of my client's 'one guiding word' (but only since doing all of the exercises in this book and writing his Life Plan) has been **'Ramifications'**.

He explains that when he just says that word to himself, it pulls him back from whatever action or comment he might have been about to make (good, bad or questionable), and he visualizes the future implications of it. If he does/says it, what future end result might he be creating?

That one guiding word and his pause to think about it ? It centers him and focuses him on *who he is becoming*, on *who he wishes to be*. It is the one word that pulls him back to his priorities, goals and keeps him working his Life Plan.

Additionally, in focusing on personal growth and making improvements in how you act and react to life's expected and unexpected events, you will find that you also have **triggers** leading to unwanted behaviors or actions — and that a trigger can likewise be one word.

What is a 'trigger'? For our purposes, it is a stimulus. In addition to being a single word, it could be a situation that occurs, or words that someone says to you that set off an automated and usually unwanted or negative reaction in you. Triggers are very personal; different stimuli trigger different people to take different actions.

Examples:

- For a committed smoker, there might be any number of 'triggers' to pick up and light a cigarette — the phone rings, a meal is over, a TV show starts, a cup of coffee is in hand, it's time to get in the car, etc. His triggers are events; they are triggers setting off the automated 'smoke now' command.

  When the smoker sees the smoking as an unhealthy habit and has a goal of quitting, knowing and short-circuiting his triggers is vital to his success.

- For someone who has tested on the DISC as a strong D (dominance) style of person, we quite often see the two traits of 'impatience' and 'interrupting others' in him. One — the natural impatience — might well be the trigger for the other — the tendency to interrupt others.

When the strong D individual sees the interrupting as a bad habit of his that sabotages his harmonious communication with others, he chooses to correct and even eliminate it by dealing with the trigger. Knowing his trigger allows him to relax, bite his tongue and take a deep breath, instead of acting on it.

Thus, we see how a single word can be **positive** — your 'one guiding word' — or **negative** — your 'trigger' to acting out a bad habit. The core strengths you have discovered, the core values you have identified, the name of the eight Life Wheel domains, are each single words and have their own type of power in your life.

Exercise: Your One Word

As the last exercise in Parts 1 & 2, and before moving into writing out your first Life Plan:

1. Think about the single word (one or more may come to mind) that positively guides and directs your life and choices and write it in the left-side column.
   - Write what that guiding word leads you to do.
2. Identify the trigger words (again, one or more) that you recognize will negatively and automatically move you to a type of action.
   - Write what that triggering word leads you to do.

Use the chart on the next page to record as many of each as come to mind.

Example:

"My One Guiding Word is '<u>respect</u>'. It leads me to bite my tongue before interrupting or saying something I will regret. Also, it gives me pause if I feel I am being disrespected by anyone; it leads me to stop and reflect about the whole context, and helps me make sure I understand what really is going on."

One Guiding Word and It Leads Me to . . .	Trigger Word and It Leads Me to . . .

Your Key Learnings — One Guiding Word & Trigger Word

What did you learn?

_____

_____

_____

_____

_____

_____

_____

What stood out?

_____

_____

_____

_____

_____

What was a surprise?

_____

_____

_____

_____

_____

What is in question?

_____

_____

_____

_____

_____

CHAPTER 16

YOUR TOP PRIORITIES

YOU HAVE BUILT a foundation of self-awareness. You have thought a bit about your priorities for the future. I am ready ... almost ... to guide you in putting your Life Plan in place in Part 3.

To recap how far you have come in this journey of self-awareness, you:

→ Identified your natural **Strengths** ... and some weaknesses
→ Know your one or two strongest **DISC** behavior styles
→ Understand your Emotional Intelligence Quotient or **EQ**
→ Know your primary and perhaps your secondary **Love Language** and started to watch for and identify the language of others
→ Identified your life **Turning Points** and some of the associated past **Decisions** they led to
→ Pondered your **Core Domains** and know how balanced (round or misshapen) your **Life Wheel** is right now
→ Considered how you might improve the flat areas of the Wheel
→ Looked at your **Time** usage and management
→ Determined your **Core Values**
→ Wrote your **Personal Mission Statement**
→ Considered the mind-opening power of **Legacy**-thinking when you set goals or create a Life Plan

You have been building up a great deal of new (or clarified) information about yourself!

I'd like to harken back to one of the exercises. The exercise on your life's **turning points** and the subsequent **decisions** you made — the decisions you made — is related to **priorities**. If in the past you made a <u>decision</u> to 'stop talking about emotions' that became a <u>priority</u> that directed a part of your behavior (and might still be doing so). That is neither always good or bad, so don't worry about them too much. But it is time to consider your priorities of *today*. Review all your notes and responses about these areas now.

Bring that information together now along with the shape of your **Wheel of Life** and its eight core domains, the **roles** you have identified for yourself, and the list of **values** as well as the **Personal Mission Statement** you just wrote about. Review all that, too.

Also review all your responses about each exercise done in Part 1 and Part 2, and those responses to the 4 questions about each of the Wheel's core domains.

Priorities List

Now let's use your review to get even clearer on **your all-important priorities**. As the name implies, it is about what is important to you, but more than that, it is about what preoccupies you most of the time or a lot of the time. Priorities also tend to direct how you spend your time — and how much of it you spend. Priorities are with you all the time, in a very real sense. You are either worrying about them or working to improve them.

The priorities you choose will be unique to you. They depend on where you are right now in your awareness, ***and where you wish to take your life***.

To consider your priorities, we go back to the Core Domains on the Wheel and look at our priorities or lack of them in each domain.

The Life Wheel I have been using with you has these eight **domains**:

1. Career
2. Finances
3. Health
4. Family
5. Romance
6. Growth
7. Fun
8. Faith

How would this prioritizing look? That is, if you look at these areas of your life, which one is the most important? Which one is least important to you?

Example:

I have a client going through the Life Planning process. Without going yet into his priorities, he knows the following things are 'true' about him and his life right now. He:

- is in less than optimal health
- has a strong spiritual life
- is spinning his wheels in the business he owns (it is not prospering)
- has a loving spouse
- gets along great with his three kids
- romance and fun are <u>flat</u> on his Wheel

What might his top three priorities look like? First, he wrote the name of the core domain and the words you see in **bold**. Then, he ranked the importance to him, and we see that Health became his top priority. Then he wrote some reasoning for each one:

#1 **Health**: **overweight**; need to drop the excess 40 pounds; eat better and exercise daily

#2 **Fun**: spend more scheduled time with the kids and spouse; out and about on **fun sport-related excursions** or 'touristy' days in town; scheduled alone 'fun' time with spouse outside the home once weekly like in the old days

#3 **Career**: hire a business consultant and **stop procrastinating about turning slumping sales around**

Now it is your turn.

Exercise: Your Priorities

Use the chart on the next page to do this exercise.

1. Start in the **Priorities Statement** column: write your Priority Statements in the table, taking your review and your new awareness into account. Write them as they come to you.

2. Next, the **left**-side column: the Rank column is for the order of importance of each item you just wrote. When you have written all the priorities you have right now, go back and give them numbers of importance, with **1** being your top priority, **2** your next one and so on. Since you wrote your priorities as they came to you, you may find your #1 priority in the middle of the list, and that is fine. Rank all priority statements you wrote.

3. Now complete the **right**-side **Reason for Ranking** column: If you rank something high, in the right-side column state why (even if it is obvious). If you rank an item rather low, ponder why it is even a priority, and write your reason in the column. You may not have comments for every priority — but give it a try!

4. Indicate in the **Role(s)** column which role — or roles — of yours is affected, involved or influenced by this Priority.

5. Note that it is fine to have, say, only 3 or 5 priorities, just as it is perfectly okay to have a dozen. We are aiming for clarity!

Rank	Priority Statement	Role(s) Involved	Reason for Ranking or Current Status of that Area

Rank	Priority Statement	Role(s) Involved	Reason for Ranking or Current Status of that Area

Rank	Priority Statement	Role(s) Involved	Reason for Ranking or Current Status of that Area

Rank	Priority Statement	Role(s) Involved	Reason for Ranking or Current Status of that Area

You have established your priorities and ranked them, so it's time to establish some rough objectives for **what you would like to see change for each priority.** We will get more specific and detailed when you create your Life Plan in the next sections of this book.

Example: My client in fact wrote 'what needs improving' right in his Priorities list — and you may have, too.

- He wrote 'hire a business consultant' in his **career** priority — he knew that he'd been putting off getting outside expert advice on fixing what was wrong in the business he owned. So he decided to change that. He stopped making excuses and procrastinating, and picked up the phone to make an appointment with the expert he'd already identified.
- For his **health** priority, he'd already acknowledged that he'd stopped exercising — so added that back to his daily priorities as an improvement.
- As for his **fun** domain, he shot two birds with one stone, so to speak, as he identified 'alone time' with his spouse for a fun outing together (it probably didn't hurt his **romance** domain, either!), right along with 'excursions' as a whole family as his way to improve that domain in his role as father.

Indeed, these fun, health and career priorities (and the 'fixes' or actions for improvement) became even more important for our client *when he saw his multiple roles* — as head of household/main provider, employer, father, spouse — *all affected in all of them*!

Even if you did what this client did, go into the next exercise to develop (as he did) the 'improvements' aspect of each priority you have. Even for the areas of life going well, such as this client's spiritual life, he wrote some thoughts about how to improve it, expand it, deepen it — make it more significant in his life. So should you, in the next exercise.

Example:

The list below is what my own Priorities List first looked like. God (Faith) is my #1 priority.

But notice how "Me" is in 2nd place on my list. Yes, as a family man, I felt guilty about placing myself above my wife and daughters. But also notice *why* it is in that position. I was moved to focus more on my personal 'health, growth and rest' because it was such a collection of worries for me at the time.

Here's the deal: I had to come to grips with the fact that if I wasn't taking care of myself, *I could not take care of anyone else.* I realized that if I did not prioritize my own needs, I could be only a minimal (or no) support for others. In other words, I realized if I am not healthy and rested, I cannot work and earn my living; if I do not work, money stops flowing in and I cannot support my family financially.

Since there will always be a rationale behind prioritizing in the way you do, don't make yourself wrong!

My List:

1. God	4. My Daughters	7. Career
2. Me — Health, Growth, Rest	5. Extended Family	8. Finances
3. My Wife	6. Friends	9. Helping Others

Exercise: Priorities Improvement Worksheet

Use the chart on the next pages to do the exercise.

1. Write your priority in the **left**-side column on the next worksheet
2. Think about thing you would like to change, do, learn, etc. to _improve_ that priority — and list that in the **right**-side 'improvements' column. Be specific.
3. Repeat for each priority

Priority Improvements Worksheet

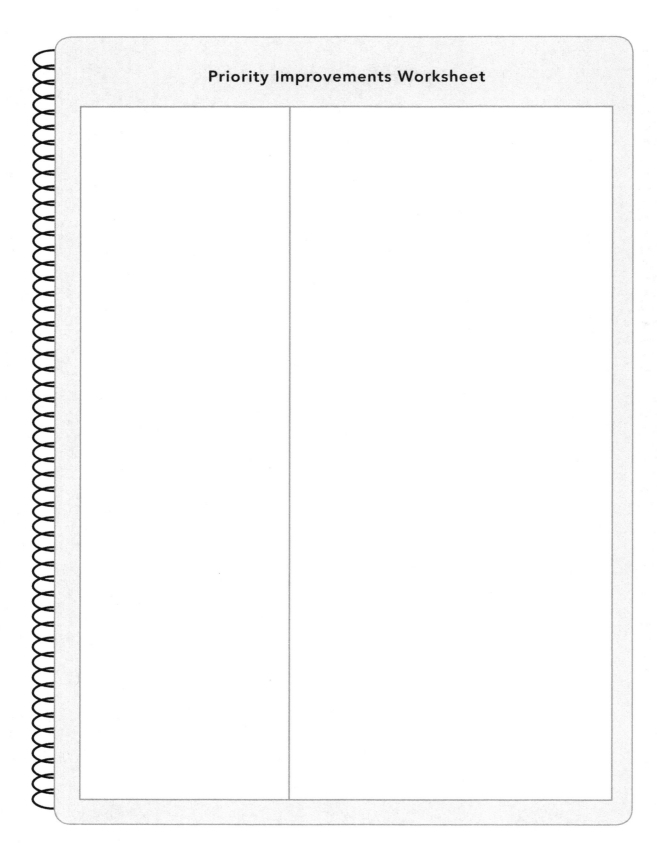

Priority Improvements Worksheet

Your Key Learnings — Your Priorities

What did you learn?

_____

_____

_____

_____

_____

_____

What stood out?

_____

_____

_____

_____

_____

What was a surprise?

_____

_____

_____

_____

What is in question?

_____

_____

_____

_____

_____

PART 3

WRITING

YOUR LIFE PLAN

THIS IS WHERE you finally write out your Life Plan. You cannot achieve a plan before you've created it, so that is your next job. But you still have a few little things to do first.

We are not forgetting any work done in Parts 1 and 2. All the exercises you have done in Part 1 and Part 2 will serve you as you create your Life Plan — those exercises and their responses are pieces of the puzzle that becomes your written Life Plan and guides you in its achievement.

From Part 1:

→ Lean more consciously from now on upon your newly-discovered Strengths. Remember what your top strengths are?

→ Anyone's current level of EQ can improve. Imagine some ways to integrate a higher level of self-regulation, social skill development and relationship management into your Life Plan.

  • Remember your own blend of D, I, S and C, and perhaps your Ah-Hah moment with the languages of love? Get support for your relationships and all your interactions from your new awareness of human behaviors and expectations, acquired through the DISC work and the Love Languages exercise, to boost yourself to a higher level of EQ.

→ Focus on the flat areas of your Wheel of Life and let your Life Plan show you how they magically fill with more air. Any area of the Wheel of Life can be the focus of one or more priorities or goals you wish to achieve as part of your Life Plan. Remind yourself which domains are flat at this time.

→ Consider past decisions made at Turning Points in your life, and whether radical or subtle changes in those decisions need to be part of your Life Plan.

→ Look again at the goals you listed at the end of Part 1 (points number 5 and 6 of that last chart). Are they still valid goals?

From Part 2:

→ Review your realizations about your Time Utilization or Time Management. Does improvement here need to be subject to a goal in your life plan?

→ Revisit your Core Value reflections. Remember your top five values? Do they still resonate strongly for you?

→ Go back to your Personal Mission Statement, reflect on whether it still represents you, who you are, and where you are going. Is it all-encompassing, or partially-encompassing, in relation to your life direction? Read it back to yourself.

→ Remind yourself of your One Guiding Word and Trigger Word.

→ Go back to your thoughts about your Legacy. Maybe you have one, maybe not yet (and either way, that is just fine).

Reviewing all of that, you were led to listing in Part 2 your **Priorities** and making **Priority Statements**, as a sort of culmination of all the exercises, introspection and new knowledge and awareness you gained. You may have discovered that some of your Priorities don't seem to fit into one of the Core Domains that I have suggested — and that is fine. All Life Plans are personal and if you have an additional or extra Core Domains from what I have suggested — follow it!

Those Priority statements really represent a list of **Outcomes** you wish to create or achieve for your life.

As you write and implement your Life Plan, always think from an <u>Outcome-based</u> perspective — the What and the Why come first. Then the How of that new result is usually apparent.

1. An outcome is the 'ultimate achievement' as it were. It is the statement of **What you want**.
2. The reason why you want this outcome — **the Why, your motivation** for this change or new circumstance — is probably more important than the What, especially in terms of staying motivated to move all the way from where you are now into where you want to be.
3. The Action Items are your **How — they are the steps you take** daily, weekly and monthly that move you into that desired outcome.

In other words? The only way to achieve your desired **outcomes** and put your **priorities** in their proper place is to be internally **motivated** and have a set of **actions** that you take — **an action plan** — to move you closer to experiencing those outcomes and rebalancing those priorities. That is where we begin.

In summary, **your Life Plan takes into account**:

- **Priorities** — stating your priorities as **goals** to be achieved in the short, medium or long term.
- **Outcomes** — improvements or **changes** in the core domains of your life.
- **Action Plans** — taking **individual actions** that achieve the goals, materialize those outcomes and have the life you have dreamed of.

Don't mistake movement (your action items) for achievements.

Your target should be <u>achievement</u>.

CHAPTER 17

HOW TO WRITE
AND SET GOALS

YOUR LIFE PLAN is going to look like a set of goals matched with a set of action items that help you achieve them. But first, what is a goal? How do you 'write' a goal so that it is more achievable?

What is a Goal?

I used to think about goals or outcomes in terms of an 'end'. I used to see them as a destination or like the hoop of a basketball court. The goal is to get there, to make that basket — and done! I thought that when I achieved the goal, that would be the end of things.

Here's the rub with that kind of thinking: No professional basketball player would ever consider stopping at that one basket! Why would you? The pro' became that by continuously going for new, additional baskets and by racking up loads of points.

With that sort of analogy (a little more maturity and patience that accumulated in me over the years), I have come to understand that setting a goal is not always a 'final destination'. It is often only part of the journey — a trip I am taking throughout life. Achieving that single goal helps future travel down my life's path to feel more pleasant, effortless and fulfilling, sure, but the next goal lines me up for even more goodness. I have realized that achieving a goal only means that my life has expanded . . . and that, far from being done, I'm ready to set the next higher, bigger goal.

> *Setting a goal is not always a 'final destination'. It is often only part of the journey.*

Why does anyone set a goal for himself? You set goals because you want more of something, or you wish to satisfy some priority you have. To create something of more value and importance to you. You see the Priority (as you did in the exercises from Parts 1 and 2), then you set the Goal to materialize it.

To illustrate how to go **from Priorities to Goals**, let's take our Part 2 client's top three priorities, which were:

#1 **Health:**   **overweight**; need to drop the excess 40 pounds; eat better and exercise daily

#2 **Fun:**   spend more scheduled time with the kids and spouse; out and about on **fun sport-related excursions** or 'touristy' days in town; scheduled alone 'fun' time with spouse outside the home once weekly like in the old days

#3 **Career:**   hire a business consultant and **stop procrastinating about turning slumping sales around**

"*Needing to drop the excess 40 pounds*" is on his priority list as #1, but this is <u>not</u> his **goal statement**! And as you will see, it is not just one single goal statement that carries him to full achievement of the weight loss. It is a collection of goals. More on that later.

Why Write Goals?

Writing — doing the actual writing out or typing out of a goal that is dear to your heart — has a magical effect on its achievement. That now-legendary Harvard survey of its Business School graduates on the subject of having/writing out their goals proved the point: <u>Writing out goals</u> is a large part of what <u>achieves them</u>! It is the thinking done before the writing, and then the actual written goal itself, which firms up your ***intention.***

Energy follows intention.

I firmly believe, as you might have guessed, in *Living Intentionally*. There is no better way to express your intention than to write out a well-considered **goal statement.**

It is not too much to predict that — once you have done all the work to understand your What, Why, and How . . . and written out your goal statement — you will achieve that written goal.

How to Write your Goals

Given the importance of a goal, then, it is wise to invest a bit of time in learning to write them effectively. This sets you up to

1. believing firmly in the goal's feasibility
2. believing in yourself and your ability to have that outcome
3. having something to visualize as you work your way toward it

There are a number of ways of writing out your goals, of finding the words to express them. The two best ones each involve 5 items to consider.

One is the well-known **SMART** approach, where the acronym stands for *Specific, Measurable, Actionable, Realistic and Timebound*. You use these five words to make sure your goal statement is complete.

Another way is the **I Decide** approach which will always start with your priority statements. They are not goal statements yet, as I stated above. To transform each of your priority statements into one or more **goal statements**, there are five steps to follow:

1. Start each statement with the words "**I decide**...". The mind says, "Well, okay then, my person has made a new decision to materialize something" and things start happening.

2. Use only **positive words** in your statement. Thus, the word "overweight" will not be part of this gentleman's statement. Why? He sees that as a negative thing he wants to change! Also, the way the mind works, any word you use is what gets created! He does not wish to perpetuate "overweight" but get

rid of it. What he chooses to create is "175 pounds or less", so he prefers this wording.

3. Add a phrase such as **"or better"**, **"or more"**, **"or sooner"** in the statement. Let the Universe decide how great a goal can be achieved on a higher plane.

4. Try to use the word **"easily"** or **"effortlessly"** in your statement. Who wants to struggle for improvement?

5. State a **deadline** for this goal's achievement. Tell the Universe (and yourself, your accountability partner) that you are in a hurry.

This transforms the "*Needing to drop the excess 40 pounds*" <u>priority</u> into a <u>goal statement</u> reading something like this . . .

<u>Priority:</u>
Need to drop the excess 40 pounds

<u>Goal:</u>
"I <u>decide</u> to <u>easily</u> achieve a body weight of 175 pounds <u>or less</u>, with great health and wellness, <u>by this June 30 or sooner</u>."

Notice how different they sound from each other? Which one <u>leads you toward it</u> and <u>which one pushes you away</u>?

You might also notice that the above goal statement is expressed from the **SMART** approach as well. It is **specific** (a weight of 175 pounds), **measurable** (hop on the scale), **actionable** (you follow your action items regarding how and what to eat, and what exercise to do), **realistic** (it is chunked down and feasible), **timebound** (by June 30th or sooner).

A '**BHAG®**' is an idea from *Built to Last*, Jim Collins' classic business book. It means **Big, Hairy, Audacious Goal** — a goal that's just a little bit out of your reach. It's one of the concepts that distinguishes great people from average ones. When creating your goal statement, you want to stretch your thinking of what you can accomplish.

Here are two reasons a BHAG — a goal you don't think you can reach — is good for you (which I thank Dave Ramsey for sharing):

1. **A BHAG is a challenge to you.** A challenge, in this case, is anything you can see but that is beyond your normal, everyday habitual reach.

   You <u>want</u> a goal that's just out of reach. Even when you stretch your muscles out, out, out . . . or jump a little, then jump again when you don't normally jump at all? It's something you can do that is . . . just beyond your *normal, everyday* habitual *reach*.

   A BHAG isn't a goal that's <u>too</u> far to ever reach — that would make you feel defeated. A BHAG inspires you to work harder and more creatively to make sure you reach that goal. There's no good reason not to reach **<u>for</u>** it or to reach **<u>it</u>**. *It's right there before your very eyes . . . at the end of your reaching fingertips.*

2. **Even if you don't reach it, your BHAG will do amazing things for you.**

   A BHAG is made to push you, to get you to try harder than you have to reach a ho-hum normal, 'anyone could do this' type of goal. So even if you don't reach it, you're still going somewhere — places you might never have thought of before. Even if you don't reach it, other great things are going to materialize for you along the way. Even if you don't reach it, you will know you are different; you feel more expanded, more energized, more powerful . . . just by having given it your all!

The Big Hairy Audacious Goal is the <u>*ultimate achievement*</u> for that core domain's priority. It is the 'destination address' you set your GPS to and head towards. It is the end result you will be aiming to achieve with all the actions you take.

Your Big Hairy Audacious Goal — your BHAG — is the ultimate achievement for that core domain's Priority.

Exercise

Use the charts on the next pages.

1. In the first chart, write each **Priority** out, in the appropriate domain.

2. Refer to the 5 steps to Writing a Goal Statement listed above — either the SMART approach or the I DECIDE approach. Take your top three Priorities and reword them into **Big Hairy Audacious Goal Statements**. Play a little with the wording to make sure you have followed the steps and have a goal that sounds like a good fit for each Priority.

3. Now do the same for all other Priorities in each of the 8 domains . . . as well as with priorities that might be outside domains I have given you.

4. You may have one or more priorities for a domain, so list them all.

5. In front of each domain name, put the number from **1 to 8** which shows where it is ranked for its importance. #1 is the highest importance, and it is urgent to start there. #8 is the lowest importance but will still be part of the Life Plan.

Your Priority Statements:

_____ **Career**

_____ **Finances**

_____ **Health**

_____ **Family**

_____ **Romance**

_____ **Growth**

_____ **Fun**

_____ **Faith**

What is Most Important to You?

Your Priorities from the previous chart, now written as the Big Hairy Audacious Goal statements, and numbered for their priority from high to low:

_____ **Career**

_____ **Finances**

_____ **Health**

_____ **Family**

_____ **Romance**

_____ **Growth**

_____ **Fun**

_____ **Faith**

Short, Medium or Long Term

You are starting to see that you have numerous goals to achieve! You might wonder how to work on so many goals at one time. Relax! You won't have to do them all at once.

You certainly have some goals that can be achieved sooner than others. So first, you determine how long each **Big Hairy Audacious Goal** might take to achieve. A week? A year? 3 years? 10 years?

- Making an article of clothing for yourself may take a few days or a week.
- Losing those last 10 pounds might be a matter of several months.
- Me finishing this workbook for you is a matter of one whole year.
- Going from no high school diploma to a completed PhD is many years.
- Leaving behind a legacy may require two decades.

A Life Plan deals with the short-term, medium-term and the long-term. A Life Plan is a map — dealing with today, next year and even 10 and 30 years down the road. Any good map has milestones that you aim for, and once you pass them you simply aim for the next milestone and so on, until you get to your destination . . . or achieve that BHAG. That is where **action items** for the immediate moment, the medium and long terms come in.

What is a short, medium or long-term in the context of a Life Plan? As with the approaches to writing out your goal statements, here are two ways to define them. My clients have seen this defined in one of two ways. Choose one. Stick with it.

First Definition of Terms

1. **Short**-term goals are achievable within **3 months (quarterly).**
2. **Medium**-term goals are achievable within **12 months (annual).**
3. **Long**-term goals are achievable within **3 to 5 years.**
4. **Life**-time or **legacy** goals are anything **beyond 5 years.**

Note that you can set any or all of these types of goals.

You may already think in terms of the above time frames, and if you are comfortable with them, use them!

Second Definition of Terms

Here is the definition of these short-, medium- and long-term time frames that I use, and it helps me stay on track in executing (or doing what I need to do) to achieve all the goals in my Life Plan:

- Life-time/legacy goals = **My purpose, direction and achievements over 10-30 Years**
- Long-term goals = **3-5 Years**
- Medium-term goals = **1 Year**
- Short-term goals = **4 Quarters of the Year**

To the above, and to help focus me during a manageable period of time, I add a:
- 1 Year Theme = my **focus for the whole year**, which fuels and accelerates its achievement
- 1 Year Metrics = **how I know I am moving forward**, using accountabilities and measurements

Use one of these time frames and place all your goals and action items within that framework in a consistent way. That helps you track progress as we will see in Part 4.

*Is your **Big Hairy Audacious Goal** too big to achieve **<u>this week</u>**?*
Probably all of them are!

You use the above framework and find a home, as it were, for all of your BHAGs. You see clearly that some are achievable quite soon (with the right action items and daily 'doing' of them), while others stretch far into a future that might be hard to envision clearly.

For all of these goals, the easiest way to achieve them and assign do-able Action Items to them is by **'chunking down the Big Hairy Audacious Goals into bite-sized pieces'.**

Remember that I said in a prior section that Goals are not a destination but a journey with many milestones? Well, the chunking-down process is how you will create your **Milestones**. Thus, for many of your BHAGs, you will need a number of **Milestone Goals** attached to them, and which you aim to achieve in the short-term framework.

Example:

Chunking down your Big Hairy Audacious Goals into Milestones is vital to achieving them!

My client's ultimate goal — his **Big Hairy Weight Loss Goal** — got defined as achievable in the *medium-term*. For this BHAG goal of dropping 40 pounds, he knew that he would not realistically achieve this goal in the short term (not in 3 months or less, much less in one week) and maintain good health and habits.

Thus, I suggested that he set one or more **Milestones** whose purpose was _to help him easily get to the larger goal without his mind resisting doing it_. The Milestones were goals, too. They represented a measurable way — by getting on the scale — to gauge his progress towards his ultimate weight loss goal.

Here is what he did:

His starting body weight was 215 pounds. In this man's mind, to lose 40 pounds total is a _medium-term_ (six or seven month) goal to achieve. Here is the **Big Hairy Audacious Goal** again, written in November:

"I decide to easily achieve the weight of 175 pounds or less, in great health and wellness, by this June 30 or sooner."

He set **a Milestone Goal** that reads like this:

"I <u>decide</u> to <u>easily</u> achieve a healthy weight of <u>205 pounds or less by the New Year</u>."

Having written this in early November, it gives him two full months to lose 10 pounds. More than enough time? He thinks so! That is how to start at any rate, since our minds can easily imagine how things will be 2 months from now. Imagining 8 months, much less 8 years, down the road is a lot harder.

What happens when he has reached 205 pounds? He states the **next Milestone Goal**:

"I <u>decide</u> to <u>easily</u> achieve a healthy weight of <u>195 pounds or less</u> by <u>Valentine's Day or sooner</u>, in great health and wellness."

Do you see how chunking down the BHAG by creating any number of Milestone Goals gives you stepping-stones that lead you to the Big Hairy Audacious Goal achievement? How it makes everything more manageable?

Can you see how the achievement of each **Milestone** brought him closer and closer to the realization of his **Big Hairy Audacious Goal?** He kept doing this and achieving those **Milestones** and achieving them in 6 or 8 weeks, until by June he had reached his **Big Hairy Audacious Goal** weight of 175 pounds.

Each milestone, when achieved, should bring you closer to the BHAG — that is the goal of the goal!

Each of these Milestones went into his Life Planning Dashboard*
along with the specific Action Items to help him achieve them.

*More on that Dashboard in the next chapter.

More Examples:

Here is how **Big Hairy Audacious Goals** could be chunked down into Milestone Goals on the journey to achievement:

Health: From a priority statement of 'Have more energy' to a BHAG statement of:

"I decide to easily choose and eat only raw vegetables and raw fruit at will as my entire lunchtime meal, starting today and continuing indefinitely."

➔ "This evening, I decide to shop in the produce section of the store and buying 3 days' worth of lunch fruit and veg."

Career: From 'Earn more money' to

"I decide to effortlessly sign one new, lucrative contract of work per month for my side business starting in January."

➔ "This week I decide to easily place an ad each day in the four sites/ papers that have been successful for me in the past."

Romance: From 'Spend more time with spouse' to

"I decide to easily, proactively reserve and organize one Us-Only outing outside the home and one Us-Only special-event evening at home per week, starting next week."

➔ "This evening, I decide to plan and write down our first two weeks' Us-Time and tell my spouse about them."

Look again at our gentleman's **Big Hairy Weight-Loss Goal**. A short-term goal of '10 pounds lighter' was achieved in **two** months by this client. His medium-term goal of '40 pounds lighter' was achieved within **eight** months.

What about this same client's career goals, the 3ʳᵈ in his top three priorities? As we saw, he listed as a **priority** to 'hire a business consultant' and sit with him to discuss problems and solutions for his 'slumping sales'. Setting an appointment is most definitely achievable right away, and so he set that as a **Milestone Goal** to be achieved within two weeks' time. That allowed for the consultant's and his own schedules to coincide for their first meeting. From there, with the consultant, he planned on setting short-term, medium-term and long-term goals — each one *appropriately chunked down into Milestone Goals and accompanied by action items* — to turn around slumping sales and increase them quite dramatically.

If you are in business, you can see that going from, say, $100,000 in sales to $1 million in sales is not really likely to be achieved by most types of businesses in <u>one year</u>. That is where some of this man's long-term goals came from — he was fairly certain he could achieve $1 million in sales by the end of year three . . . if he set and achieved all his Milestone Goals all along the way.

**Setting your Milestone Goals along the way keeps you on track
as you take actions each day.**

**Setting your Milestone Goals keeps you motivated
to achieve your BHAG!**

CHAPTER 18

WRITING YOUR LIFE PLAN

THIS IS IT! Time to write out your personalized Life Plan!

You never hit a target you don't have. The BHAGs are your <u>ultimate targets</u>. Your Milestone Goals, written in the same way as your BHAG statements, are your secondary markers on your way to BHAG achievement.

The Milestones are the immediate targets — right in front of you all the time —helping you hit the more distant BHAG.

Your Envisioned Future Per Domain

Your '**envisioned future**' (as I like to call it) is simply your '**desired outcome**'. You now see them all expressed as **Big Hairy Audacious Goals**. I guided you through discovering those BHAGs through the tool called the Life Wheel, which presents eight important aspects of life called Core Domains, for which you developed a Priorities List.

For memory, here are the domains most of my clients focus on in their Life Plans*:

1. Career
2. Finances
3. Health
4. Family

5. Romance
6. Growth
7. Fun
8. Faith

***Reminder**: The above eight domains help *most* people look at all aspects of their life. Feel 100% free, however, to reduce them to the basic 5 of Growth, Health, Family, Faith and Career if all eight overwhelm you. Contrarily, you can surely add additional domains to my eight — or simply to rename them to appeal to you better — to further personalize your Plan and address all aspects of your own life.

Writing Approach

Your Life Plan will be written, as I illustrate below, on several pages of paper. The first page is a sort of 'Index' I created for my entire Life Plan. You start with your personalized Index, then move into the Plan for each Big Hairy Audacious Goal — as you see mapped out for you in the next pages.

The chart below is my own map to illustrate what you will do:

Priorities

What is most important to you?

Priority	Additional Information
God	Morning, Pre-Work Devotionals & Prayer; Relationship with God
Self	Health, Growth, Rest
Spouse	Together: Time, Relationship, Fun, Rest — Vacation/Time to Refuel
Children	Abby, Allison, Emily
Friends	XXX
Extended Family	Brad/Family, Sheila/Family, Colleen/Family
Career	See the Strategic Plan created for the business, and timeline, goals and flags
Finances	XXX
Ministry	My 'Give Back Initiative' (GBI)

You see that issues around finances and friends were <u>not</u> top priorities for me (I put XXX through those items), as they might be for someone else. I added "Ministry", which is meaningful to me, but perhaps not to anyone else. That is what makes your Life Plan so personal — it is not others who impose it on you; you get to decide what is valuable and important for yourself. Whence the exercises of Parts 1 and 2!

In the next chart you complete your own Index. Notice that you get to fill in your own Core Domains under the Priorities heading of the left-side column — make this your own, starting right now!

Priorities

What is most important to you? Fill in your own Index. I have inserted extra lines (which my own Plan did not require), in the case you have more Priorities to note than I did.

Priority	Additional Information
1.	
2.	
3.	
4.	
5.	
6.	
7.	
8.	
9.	
10.	
11.	
12.	

On the next page is what <u>one whole entry</u> in my own **Life Plan** looks like. This sample page is for my **Priority #2 'Self',** specifically **'Rest'.**

I have written out such a chart or page for each of the Priorities on the above 'Index' of my Life Plan — and so will you.

Each page includes:

1. a statement of your **Desired Outcome (Envisioned Future)**
2. a reminder statement about why it is important to you to achieve this outcome **(Why or Purpose Statement)**
3. a supporting **Verse** or **Inspirational** quotation if you wish
4. a statement or bullet points showing your **Current Reality** or **Starting Point** that you will be in some way changing
5. the **Action Items** to perform (or **Commitments** you are willing to make) in order to achieve the Envisioned Future.

The following page is 'ripped', so to speak, from my own actual Life Plan simply to illustrate what you will do next:

What is most important to me?

PRIORITY	SELF - HEALTH

ENVISIONED FUTURE (DESIRED OUTCOME)

I am 155 pounds of lean muscle. I am doing cardio every day and working out with weights 4 times a week. I run 1 10k or half-marathon a year. I maintain bodyfat of 18% or better with 18 inch arms and a six pack of abs.

BHAG

Maintain working out everyday, 18" arms and six pack until age 70.

PURPOSE STATEMENT (WHY)

My purpose is to maintain what God has blessed me with (my body/temple). I would like to physical grow in size and strength to maintain my health to continue to do His work. This will allow me to execute on my priorities and One Page Life Plan.

INSPIRATION OR SUPPORTING VERSE

You don't appreciate your health until you don't have it any longer.

CURRENT REALITY / STARTING POINT

- Working out every day on cardio, but need to change routines
- Not eating as healthy as I can
- Drinking a little too much
- Not having consistent weight workouts

SPECIFIC COMMITMENTS (ACTION ITEMS)

- Workout every day and monitor health activity
- Workout with weights 4x week and track workouts and results in strong app
- Measure results monthly against my envisioned future
- Get 7 hours of sleep nightly
- Get annual check ups

It's Your Life	*Live On Purpose*	*Time is Our Only Non-Renewal Resource*

Writing Your Whole Plan

This is it! You now write your entire Life Plan using the blank charts on the next pages as your template.

Complete such sheets for each **Big Hairy Audacious Goal** you have set. That way, you are sure to memorialize all of your **Priorities**. By having them all in writing, you will be able to easily execute on them (and we'll see how to do that in the detail in the next section).

Use the following blank pages as your template and do the writing now.

If you are a digitally-comfortable person, just replicate the charts in an Excel or Word document and write it up.

You also can download the template at **www.craigsroda.com**.

If you prefer to write by hand, that is great, too.

Just get writing!

Note: There are 13 templates included for your convenience. Usually people have around 5 priorities, but these priorities may change over time. As your priorities change, you can use the extra templates to write more. *Don't feel like you need to fill out every single chart right away!*

Priorities: What is important to me?

PRIORITY: _____

ENVISIONED FUTURE (DESIRED OUTCOME)

BHAG

PURPOSE STATEMENT (WHY)

INSPIRATION OR SUPPORTING VERSE

CURRENT REALITY / STARTING POINT

-
-
-
-
-
-

SPECIFIC COMMITMENTS (ACTION ITEMS)

-
-
-
-
-
-
-

Priorities: What is important to me?

PRIORITY: _____

ENVISIONED FUTURE (DESIRED OUTCOME)

BHAG

PURPOSE STATEMENT (WHY)

INSPIRATION OR SUPPORTING VERSE

CURRENT REALITY / STARTING POINT

-
-
-
-
-
-

SPECIFIC COMMITMENTS (ACTION ITEMS)

-
-
-
-
-
-
-

Priorities: What is important to me?

PRIORITY: _____

ENVISIONED FUTURE (DESIRED OUTCOME)

BHAG

PURPOSE STATEMENT (WHY)

INSPIRATION OR SUPPORTING VERSE

CURRENT REALITY / STARTING POINT

-
-
-
-
-
-

SPECIFIC COMMITMENTS (ACTION ITEMS)

-
-
-
-
-
-
-
-

It's Your Life   *Live On Purpose*   *Time is Our Only Non-Renewal Resource*

Priorities: What is important to me?

PRIORITY: _____

ENVISIONED FUTURE (DESIRED OUTCOME)

BHAG

PURPOSE STATEMENT (WHY)

INSPIRATION OR SUPPORTING VERSE

CURRENT REALITY / STARTING POINT

-
-
-
-
-
-

SPECIFIC COMMITMENTS (ACTION ITEMS)

-
-
-
-
-
-
-
-

Priorities: What is important to me?

PRIORITY: _____

ENVISIONED FUTURE (DESIRED OUTCOME)

BHAG

PURPOSE STATEMENT (WHY)

INSPIRATION OR SUPPORTING VERSE

CURRENT REALITY / STARTING POINT

- •
- •
- •
- •
- •
- •

SPECIFIC COMMITMENTS (ACTION ITEMS)

- •
- •
- •
- •
- •
- •
- •

It's Your Life   *Live On Purpose*   *Time is Our Only Non-Renewal Resource*

Priorities: What is important to me?

PRIORITY: _____

ENVISIONED FUTURE (DESIRED OUTCOME)

BHAG

PURPOSE STATEMENT (WHY)

INSPIRATION OR SUPPORTING VERSE

CURRENT REALITY / STARTING POINT
-
-
-
-
-
-

SPECIFIC COMMITMENTS (ACTION ITEMS)
-
-
-
-
-
-
-

Priorities: What is important to me?

PRIORITY: _____

ENVISIONED FUTURE (DESIRED OUTCOME)

BHAG

PURPOSE STATEMENT (WHY)

INSPIRATION OR SUPPORTING VERSE

CURRENT REALITY / STARTING POINT

-
-
-
-
-
-

SPECIFIC COMMITMENTS (ACTION ITEMS)

-
-
-
-
-
-
-

Priorities: What is important to me?

PRIORITY: _____

ENVISIONED FUTURE (DESIRED OUTCOME)

BHAG

PURPOSE STATEMENT (WHY)

INSPIRATION OR SUPPORTING VERSE

CURRENT REALITY / STARTING POINT

-
-
-
-
-
-

SPECIFIC COMMITMENTS (ACTION ITEMS)

-
-
-
-
-
-
-

It's Your Life   *Live On Purpose*   *Time is Our Only Non-Renewal Resource*

Priorities: What is important to me?

PRIORITY: _____

ENVISIONED FUTURE (DESIRED OUTCOME)

BHAG

PURPOSE STATEMENT (WHY)

INSPIRATION OR SUPPORTING VERSE

CURRENT REALITY / STARTING POINT

-
-
-
-
-
-

SPECIFIC COMMITMENTS (ACTION ITEMS)

-
-
-
-
-
-
-

It's Your Life   *Live On Purpose*   *Time is Our Only Non-Renewal Resource*

Priorities: What is important to me?

PRIORITY: _____

ENVISIONED FUTURE (DESIRED OUTCOME)

BHAG

PURPOSE STATEMENT (WHY)

INSPIRATION OR SUPPORTING VERSE

CURRENT REALITY / STARTING POINT

-
-
-
-
-
-

SPECIFIC COMMITMENTS (ACTION ITEMS)

-
-
-
-
-
-
-

Priorities: What is important to me?

PRIORITY: _____

ENVISIONED FUTURE (DESIRED OUTCOME)

BHAG

PURPOSE STATEMENT (WHY)

INSPIRATION OR SUPPORTING VERSE

CURRENT REALITY / STARTING POINT

-
-
-
-
-
-

SPECIFIC COMMITMENTS (ACTION ITEMS)

-
-
-
-
-
-
-

It's Your Life   *Live On Purpose*   *Time is Our Only Non-Renewal Resource*

Priorities: What is important to me?

PRIORITY: _____

ENVISIONED FUTURE (DESIRED OUTCOME)

BHAG

PURPOSE STATEMENT (WHY)

INSPIRATION OR SUPPORTING VERSE

CURRENT REALITY / STARTING POINT

-
-
-
-
-
-

SPECIFIC COMMITMENTS (ACTION ITEMS)

-
-
-
-
-
-

It's Your Life   *Live On Purpose*   *Time is Our Only Non-Renewal Resource*

Priorities: What is important to me?

PRIORITY: _____

ENVISIONED FUTURE (DESIRED OUTCOME)

BHAG

PURPOSE STATEMENT (WHY)

INSPIRATION OR SUPPORTING VERSE

CURRENT REALITY / STARTING POINT

- •
- •
- •
- •
- •
- •

SPECIFIC COMMITMENTS (ACTION ITEMS)

- •
- •
- •
- •
- •
- •
- •

You see that you end up with a small booklet of pages containing your Life Plan. Can it be presented differently, so that you see it all at a glance, perhaps on just one piece of paper?

Yes, and that is what the next chapter is all about.

CHAPTER 19

DISTILLING YOUR PLAN:
THE DASHBOARD APPROACH

I AM GOING to show you a great way to write out your Life Plan on one page. I call it a **One-Page Life Planning Dashboard** — or just the '**Dashboard**' — and it will further simplify the executing or achieving of your Life Plan.

Your **Dashboard** is derived from the multiple Life Plan pages which you have just written in the previous exercise. There is no one model, so I will give you a couple of options to materialize your own Dashboard.

Refer, Refer and Refer!

You want to be able to refer back to your Life Plan and the Action Items throughout the day, every single day. Refer, refer and refer again to it so that you stay on track. I know I do this. The Dashboard approach makes it easier.

A **One-Page Life Plan Dashboard** can be created or printed out:

- as an Excel worksheet or a Word document (this is for those of you who are 'digitally comfortable')
- on a huge whiteboard, that only you access or use (like some of my clients have in their home offices)
- on large paper-board sheets that you post on a private wall of your office or home (for my 'low-tech' clients, or for those who like to see everything in their own handwriting)
- In a bound notebook that you've written everything into and which you carry around all the time

I have clients who have used all of the above ways of writing out and having ready access to their Life Plans throughout the day. You may be a low-tech sort of person and prefer pen-and-paper in a bound notebook. You may carry a large bag or briefcase around, so that carrying a paper notebook or agenda book is practical. Or you may be a high-tech 'digitally comfortable' person — carrying around a tablet or laptop — and type it all out in a software application that suits you, using calendared reminder alarms for action items and so on.

The key is to 'memorialize' your Life Plan in a **written** format. You need to be able to put your eyes on it at any time of day!

Write it out in some way that works for you
so that you can refer to your Life Plan throughout the day.

And this is why a Dashboard is so useful: The point of a **One-Page Life Plan Dashboard** is to have your entire Plan in front of you every day (Have I repeated that enough? It is so very important!) . . . and thus to keep you focused on doing your Action Items day after day.

In a Spreadsheet

You can create your Life Plan Dashboard on an Excel worksheet or other software application.

In my template example on the next pages, I have filled it out for my own Life Plan. You will notice that my dashboard is for one year, 2018.

Here is how it works (and feel free to reorganize it to suit you):

The **bottom half** of the Dashboard, under the orange line labeled "YOU", reminds you of the foundation *from which* you are 'leaping' up into the top half of the Dashboard:

From Left to Right:

- 16 Personalities — your result and brief description
- Your Top 5 Strengths — from the StrengthsFinder assessment (if you have chosen not to pay for this while doing these workbook exercises, invest the 10 or so dollars and the time to do it in the next weeks)
- Behavior style — from the DISC assessment (write your numerical scores for each of the patterns)
- Love Language (I have put the top 2 for myself, as I needed that reminder — write at least the top one you have found)
- Emotional Intelligence scores — to remind you that some of your BHAG will serve to increase those scores and thus your EQ (write your numerical scores for each item)
- My Brand Promise in the lower right box derive — from your Mission Statement and Legacy exercises

The **<u>top half</u>** of the Dashboard, from left to right:

Column 1

- The Core Values and Beliefs remind you of your context.
- The Must-Do's . . . or Else items are those daily action items that you have committed to.

    Example: You note that I don't get my evening glass of spirits **unless** I have done my daily workout (I MUST work out that day OR ELSE I don't get that drink!). You might consider a minor reward or punishment that you apply to your most urgent and important Must-Do's.

- The Must-Do's for Refueling are different. They concern actions you take to 1) stay focused on the achievement of your Milestones and 2) energized of mind and body and spirit (good energy levels) throughout the days/weeks of working your Life Plan.

Examples: For some, it's playing with your young kids or grandkids on a regular basis or shooting hoops with neighbors ... drinking your afternoon 'green juice' instead of another cup of coffee or a beer ... listening to energizing dance music for 15 minutes a day; etc.

Column 2

I like to think of these items as 'why we wake up'.

- Personal Accomplishments (and Professional Accomplishments, if you wish, which is why I added a space for it) guide you over your year, but also over a lifetime. Writing them here serves as a reminder of them so that they become ingrained as a new mindset and direction for you.

- Vision is what you wish to *see* as a materialized result of your life's work — what you have accomplished. These can also be divided into Personal and Professional statements, and likewise serve to create a direction for your mind to take you to.

Column 3

- The whole column repeats the 5 core domains of Personal Growth, Family, Career, Community and Faith (or your own expanded number of domains), and are a reminder of your Legacy. Bringing focus to these 5 (even though BHAG concern the other Life Wheel domains) reminds you about *balance.* Here is primarily a Legacy question: You will be stating how you wish people to remember you when you are gone — in each of these domains.

Column 4

This is for this year's BHAG's — the Big Hairy Audacious Goals that you are working towards (even when the whole year is just its Milestone Goals) <u>anytime in this year.</u>

- Theme: Those of you with a 'One BHAG at a Time' approach will easily find the 'theme' of your year's work. It will be a statement about that single goal you chose to work on and get closer to or to achieve.

    Example: "I create greater health, accompanied by more physical energy and mental clarity, through these actions taken for my health." Or you just write "Better health and energy" as your Theme.

- For those working several BHAG's during this single year, you might do a sort of 'combo-theme' statement, however short or long. It sort of 'daisy-chains' your multiple goals into a memorable statement.

    Example: For goals dealing with the Family and Faith and Fun domains, "I have great **fun** connecting more often with **family** and my religious **faith** and its community." Or you just write "Fun, Family, Faith" which name the key words of your BHAG's.

- Your 1-Year Goals/Priorities will list — in keyword form — each BHAG you are working on <u>anytime in this year.</u>

    Examples:
    - Health/6-pack abs
    - Career/12,000 new followers on my social media
    - Family/3 evenings of Just-Us-Time weekly

- Critical Actions/Numbers will support the achievement of the Milestones and BHAG. These are all about "what you have to do" to achieve goals with dollars, numbers, weight, dates, etc. — measures of some kind that you have added to any of your Goal Statements.

Examples:

- Health/170 pounds by year-end
- Faith/morning devotional time on my own, daily/15 minutes
- Reduce commute time by 50% by year-end

You notice that my Goals/Priorities are numbered and correspond numerically to my Critical Actions. That is, Goal #1 requires Critical Actions/Numbers #1, etc.

Column 5

This is where you note your Milestones Goals (which, you recall, are Goals in their own right) and any BHAG when it is achievable within your one-year Dashboard timeframe (for short and medium term goals).

Divide things up into Quarters, or 3-month segments. Have a maximum of 4 per quarter. They will typically tie into not only your Milestone Goals or BHAG, but your Legacy and Missions. They focus you to stay on track.

Quarter 1 is January, February, March
Quarter 2 is April, May, June
Quarter 3 is July, August, September
Quarter 4 is October, November, December

Within that segment, write the Action Item, Goal achievement due date:

Example: Look at my own **Dashboard.** You see in my own segments that my BHAG of 17 ½ inch upper arms through exercise starts from where I am (less than 17 inches) and so for Quarter 1 my Milestone is to achieve '17-inch' arms. I increase that with the following 17 ¼-inch Milestone, to be achieved within Quarter 2. I assume that I have achieved that Milestone and then aim for the BHAG of 17 ½ inches in Quarter 3 (from where my objective is to maintain that strength and measurement).

*Keep in mind that your **Dashboard** is yours to finetune and change as time rolls on.*

Example: Maybe you are quite clear about all Quarters goals/action items. Maybe not. In Quarter 4 — nine months out from the time you wrote up this year's One Page Life Plan™ Dashboard — I have put '**TBD**', or To Be Determined, after those 2 goals. I will be choosing one of those two events to participate in, and January was just too soon to do that. What was not too soon was knowing that <u>one</u> of them would happen!

Review how I have filled in the template for myself on the next page.

Then, complete your own **Dashboard** in the blank template!

You can also download the Word version of the template
at **www.craigsroda.com**.

CORE VALUES / BELIEFS (Yes/No Decisions) FOREVER

CORE VALUES
- Do the Wise Thing
- Family First
- Help Others
- Have Fun
- Learn Forever to Make a Difference

HARD RULES
- No Workout = No Drink
- Workout Everyday
- Mindfulness Morning Routine Everyday

REPLENISHMENT
- AM/Morning Routine
- Daily Devotional
- Exercise Daily – Cardio
- Exercise Weights – 3x/Week
- Monthly Get Aways
- Quarterly Vacations

PURPOSE / MISSION (Why) 10-30 YEARS

PURPOSE

Personal
Help Others Be Better Than They Thought They Could Be.

Inspire Others to Know Their Strengths, Understand Their Why, and Live and Intentional Life.

Professional
Build Leaders and Teams, Align Strategy, Align Priorities, Utilize Technology for Exponential Growth.

MISSION / VISION

Personal
100,000 Life Plans Influenced by 2025

Professional
Lebermuth – 100M by 2020
Lebermuth Prep for 1 Billion

LEGACY / TARGETS (How Remembered/Eulogy) NOW TO FOREVER

WHAT PEOPLE WILL SAY ABOUT

Personal
Craig always wanted to help me be better.

Family
Craig prioritized his family and helping them understand character and defining true success.

Vocation/Career
Craig prioritized truth, clarity and trust to build culture and teamwork. Craig continually wanted us to be the best version of ourselves.

Community
Craig was always striving for others to know their strengths and live on purpose.

Faith
God was Craig's foundation he didn't wear it on his shirt sleeve but I knew he was a faith guy.

GOALS / PRIORITIES (What) ANNUAL

THEME
Genuine and Authentic
Fun and Truth

1 YEAR GOALS/PRIORITIES
1. 17 ½" Arms / Six Pack
2. Book Launch / 100k
3. Lebermuth 50M
4. 1,000 Dedicated Followers
5. Dedicated Family Time

CRITICAL ACTIONS/NUMBERS
1. 17 ½" Arms
2. 2 Books Per Month
3. Net Worth by 2022 = $X
4. Family Time – Hard Stops
5. Work Hours – 50 Hours/Wk

GOALS / PRIORITIES (How) QUARTERLY

QUARTER 1	WHEN
Six Pack / 17" Arms	03/31/18
Book #3 Finish	03/31/18
Lebermuth A-Team	03/31/18

QUARTER 2	WHEN
Book #3 Launch	
Infusionsoft	
17 ½" Arms	

QUARTER 3	WHEN
IFEAT Conference	9/9-13
17 ½" Arms	
OPLP Bus. Plan	
Move In New House	

QUARTER 4	WHEN
Goldsmith Cert	tbd
EO University	tbd
OPLP – 50k	

MY BRAND PROMISE
- Help Others Know and Maximize Their Strengths
- Help Others Know Their Why
- Help Others Live on Purpose
- Align Teams for Execution

YOU

STRENGTHS FINDER 2.0 (5)
1. Futuristic
2. Strategic
3. Focused
4. Achiever
5. Responsible

16 PERSONALITIES

PROTAGONIST (ENFJ)
Protagonists are natural-born leaders, full of passion and charisma. Forming around two percent of the population, they are oftentimes our politicians, our coaches and our teachers, reaching out and inspiring others to achieve and to do good in the world. With a natural confidence that begets influence, Protagonists take a great deal of pride and joy in guiding others to work together to improve themselves and their community.

DISC

NATURAL STYLE	
D - Dominance	92
I - Influencing	72
S - Steadiness	12
C - Compliance	22

ADAPTIVE STYLE	
D - Dominance	88
I - Influencing	82
S - Steadiness	12
C - Compliance	24

EMOTIONAL

LOVE LANGUAGE	
Primary	Touch
Secondary	Time

EMOTIONAL INTELLIGENCE	
Self-Awareness	9.1
Self-Regulation	8.8
Motivation	8.7
Empathy	8.4
Social Skills	8.5
Total EI/EQ	8.7

ONE PAGE LIFE PLAN (OPLP) ™

CORE VALUES / BELIEFS
(Yes/No Decisions)
FOREVER

CORE VALUES

- • • • • •

HARD RULES

- • • • •

REPLENISHMENT

- • • • • • • •

PURPOSE / MISSION
(Why)
10-30 YEARS

PURPOSE

Personal

Professional

MISSION / VISION

Personal

Professional

LEGACY / TARGETS
(How Remembered/Eulogy)
NOW TO FOREVER

WHAT PEOPLE WILL SAY ABOUT

Personal

Family

Vocation/Career

Community

Faith

GOALS / PRIORITIES
(What)
ANNUAL

THEME

1 YEAR GOALS/PRIORITIES

1.
2.
3.
4.
5.

CRITICAL ACTIONS/NUMBERS

1.
2.
3.
4.
5.

GOALS / PRIORITIES
(How)
QUARTERLY

QUARTER 1	WHEN

QUARTER 2	WHEN

QUARTER 3	WHEN

QUARTER 4	WHEN

YOU

16 PERSONALITIES

STRENGTHS FINDER 2.0 (5)

DISC

NATURAL STYLE
- D – Dominance
- I – Influencing
- S – Steadiness
- C – Compliance

ADAPTIVE STYLE
- D – Dominance
- I – Influencing
- S – Steadiness
- C – Compliance

EMOTIONAL

LOVE LANGUAGE
- Primary
- Secondary

EMOTIONAL INTELLIGENCE
- Self-Awareness
- Self-Regulation
- Motivation
- Empathy
- Social Skills
- Total EI/EQ

MY BRAND PROMISE

- • • • •

You Don't Plan to Fail – You Fail to Plan

Live On Purpose

Writing the Dashboard on a Whiteboard or Paper Wall Chart

If my personal favorite template that I've just presented doesn't "do it for you", that is fine. The objective is to find a One Page version of your Life Plan and its Milestones and BHAG for this year that works for you.

Keep in mind you will want to see it daily (refer, refer, refer!), so it needs to be where you are or where you go.

The process is really the same for writing up your **Dashboard** on a whiteboard or paper wall chart. However, if you travel a lot, a wall-mounted whiteboard **Dashboard** won't follow you around, nor will a paperboard version. Thus, you'll need an additional or alternative solution for having it with you during trips. You can always take a picture of it from your phone so you can look at it daily/weekly.

Or, you can create a version such as in the blank *Mind Map* format, which I give you on the next page. Your Mission Statement goes in the center box. Your Big Hairy Audacious Goals go in the first boxes shooting from the center Mission Statement box. Your Milestones are then added in one, two or all three of the boxes connected to the BHAG box.

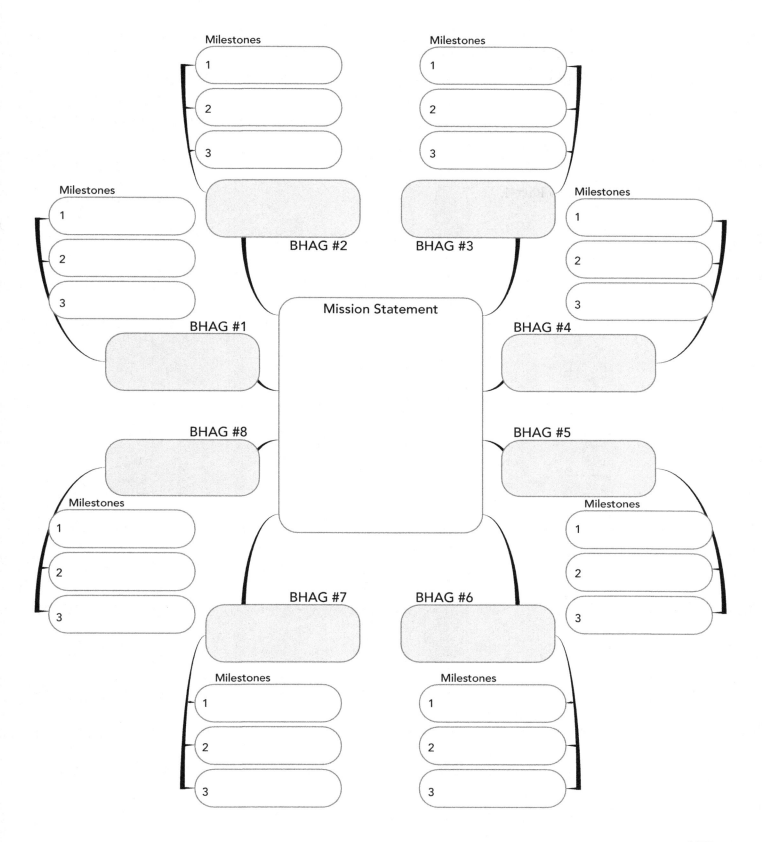

I will explain how to consult and use your **Dashboard** in Part 4 in your **'Life Plan Execution Process'**.

Whether from my template, or an idea of your own, go ahead and create your **One-Page Life Plan Dashboard** now, in any way that works for you. The main thing is to have it in a form that you will look at daily.

Then go on to Part 4.

PART 4

NOT EXCUSES

IN PART ONE and Two, you got to know yourself. You thought about your values and your priorities.

In Part Three, you learned about **Big Hairy Audacious Goals** and **Milestone Goals**. You learned how to write them for easiest achievement, so that your mind works with you, not against you. You wrote your **Life Plan** on several pages and saw how your life priorities and desired outcomes are an integral part of the Plan now . . . as are the **BHAGs** and the **Milestones**.

You have seen that your goals are not all short-term, not quickly achievable within the next 3 or 4 months. Some of them would take up to a year to achieve, while others will take you well over 5 years (career advancement or education/degree goals, certain health goals, etc.) . . . or 30 years (legacy goals, wealth-building for retirement goals, etc.).

The Advantage of Control

Having goals achievable over different lengths of time is not really a problem. It is a great _advantage_.

It might be overwhelming to think you 'must' achieve all your goals at once. But then, faced with that mountain to climb, you might be tempted to give up. No, you really don't have to achieve your goals all at once, as I have demonstrated.

You take control and make things much easier by chunking those middle-term, long-term and life-time goals down into intermediary **Milestone Goals**. They are really like short-term goals, as you have seen. Then, by assigning **Action Items** — things you do for the attainment of each of those Milestones — you gain even more control.

You control the actions you take — and you control that you take action.

Again, you have control over the achievement of each BHAG — by breaking it down into Milestones, then taking one action at a time to achieve Milestone after Milestone, all the way to BHAG achievement.

WE START AND END WITH THE BHAG

BY SETTING AND ACHIEVING **A SERIES OF MILESTONES** AND THE **ACTION ITEMS** TO ACHIEVE EACH OF THEM

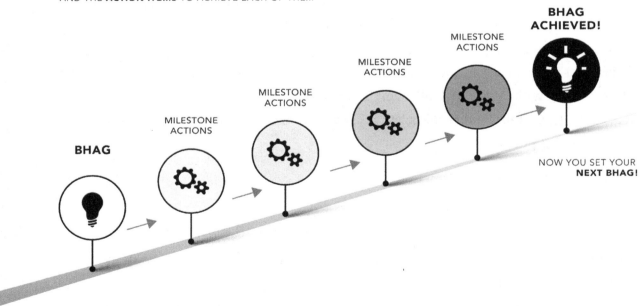

Taking effortless actions day after day is key to controlling your direction in life. Take control by performing _actions_ that achieve successive _Milestone Goals_ that lead to _BHAG_ success!

Doing something *each day* gives you **control over the realization of your entire Life Plan**:

A. **Big Hairy Audacious Goals (BHAG): Top priorities** (found in Parts One and Two) are now stated as **goals**. They are categorized into the following time frames of achievement:

1. short-term
2. medium-term
3. long-term
4. lifetime

B. **Milestones:** Each **BHAG** is chunked down into several **Milestone Goals**. These are shorter-term goals, each of which has a due date—a date at which you know you have achieved that goal.

C. **Action Items:** Each **Milestone** has one or more **Action Items** to be done (and a note on how often to do them). Some action items are performed or completed daily, others weekly, and so on. The action items are devised to help you achieve the **Milestones** within the time allotted.

D. Each **Action Item** leads to the achievement of the **Milestone**.

CHAPTER 20

LIFE PLAN ACHIEVEMENT

Achieving your Life Plan is about making — and keeping — appointments...
<u>with yourself!</u>

NOW WHAT? YOU go about implementing or '**doing**' your written plan!

As the Nike sport-shoe people so famously said, "Just Do It." This is fairly easy to tell you about in three steps:

1. **Plan and prioritize your day.** Do it every day at the same time, reminding yourself of all the Action Items for that day.
2. **See and feel each BHAG and each MILESTONE GOAL.** Feel and see it as if it has <u>already</u> materialized. Visualize and imagine it as <u>already</u> achieved.
3. **Do it from a supportive mindset**. Have an attitude of "This is for <u>me</u>; <u>I get</u> to do this; I do this <u>easily</u>."

You execute or carry out your plan. However, the 'saying' part is easy for anyone. The actual 'doing' is where we all get stuck at some point or other. If you doubt that, just look at how long people around you (or you) stick to achieving that New Year's Resolution every January!

> *Our stuckness happens right at that word 'action'.*
> *Suddenly, like magic, we have many other better things to do.*
> *Suddenly, excuses are running your day...*
> *and <u>ruining</u> your best laid (life) plan!*

Not anymore! Here in the next pages is your "Plan for Achieving the Plan". It includes the Dashboard with your BHAG and Milestone Goals on it and the Action Item schedule corresponding to each Milestone.

GPS: Your One Page Dashboard

Your **One Page Dashboard** — written up and shown in Part 3 — will serve as your daily reminder of the direction you are heading. Keep it close. Keep it visible.

You created that **Dashboard** in a way that works for you — on a digital spreadsheet, with paper and pencil, or a paper board or white board that you alone control and see, etc.

Refer to it often. Read the **Dashboard** every day, either out loud to yourself in private, or silently in your mind — but in both cases, with great attention and focus to it. See it all as already achieved. Visualize or speak out the words that describe your 'new' life when the goals are all achieved.

Action Item List: Do Something Daily

The **purpose of your Action Item List** is to give you concrete *things to do* every day, every week and every month toward the achievement of your Milestones and your Big Hairy Audacious Goals . . . and thus of your Life Plan.

I write every day's action items in some form of agenda book (paper and pen or digital), since it sets up the action item as an 'appointment' for me. In my business life I would never consider ignoring an appointment! Why would I ignore an appointment 'with myself'?

Example: The Lifetime BHAG

Going from no high school diploma to a PhD — <u>which is the exact case for one of my clients</u> — is quite a long-term goal. This is what my client decided to achieve, his priority:

"Get my PhD"

This is his Big Hairy Audacious Goal, and it then becomes:

"I decide to earn my PhD in Social Work . . .
before my own children graduate from college."

He had no diploma at all when he set the goal. Therefore, he had to set some obvious intermediary Milestone Goals to help him reach this BHAG!

Together, he and I carefully considered the timing and <u>action items</u> for some appropriate Milestone Goals — some of which were

- getting a reading tutor and systematically gaining more reading speed, comprehension and an expanded vocabulary
- finding out where to sign up for a GED program
- enrolling in the GED preparatory classes
- buying notebooks to take notes

You get the idea. This client preferred a paper **Dashboard** on his wall and an agenda book for action items and wrote everything in it.

What we also additionally discussed together were the risks associated with not doing one or more action items each and every day until he received his coveted PhD. He quickly saw that ignoring action for a day, much less for a whole week, could push back the achievement of this Big Hairy Audacious Goal by . . . years! The Milestones and their related Action Items were vital motivation for this adult student to keep on moving towards his BHAG achievement.

Don't be your own biggest obstacle to achieving your lifetime dreams! Make sure you do something each and every day, even — especially — for that far off, lifetime goal.

But the realization of a BHAG based on a short-term time frame must also start today and continue daily until completed.

Example: The Short-Term BHAG

One of our family friends is an outstanding, highly skilled seamstress. She makes virtually all of her own clothing, both casual and quite dressy. She was going to be attending a formal family event in six weeks' time, and knew she wanted to create **a brand-new 'dressy dress'** for the occasion. So, even for this very short-term goal, and with this activity she knew by heart, she used the BHAG Achievement process she learned with me to create her goals, her Milestones and her Action Items:

BHAG: "I decide to wear a beautiful new, easily self-made dress to the family event taking place on _____ (in six weeks from today)."

1st MILESTONE: "I decide to have my pattern, material and notions by the end of this week."

Action Items:
Monday — choose the pattern.
Tuesday — list all notions and material needed to create that dress.
Wednesday — visit my three favorite craft stores to fill my shopping list.
Thursday — everything I need is now purchased.

2nd MILESTONE: "I decide to complete my dress by _____ (in three weeks after completing my shopping)."

Action Items:
Monday evening — prepare the fabric and the pattern
Tuesday evening — do the ironing, pinning and cutting
Etc.

The Essential Tracking Work

I can hear your first reaction to this short-term goal right now. You are saying that for such a short-term, obvious goal — especially one that this person has achieved so many times in the past — you don't need a BHAG, much less any Milestones or Action Item list in any written form.

<u>Wrong!</u>

Your life plan does <u>not</u> contain just one Milestone or one Action Item per day.

To achieve more than one Big Hairy Audacious Goal, you will have many Milestones and Action Items going each day.

Just as our PhD client needed to focus on one step at a time, so did the seamstress. She not only — like you — had other goals and action items for those other goals. She also had 'life' — taking care of her kids, going to work and being the best she could be at her job, shopping for the family, etc.

She wrote and scheduled her Action Items so that she would have time to achieve her BHAG — even as busy as she was every day. Keep that in mind if you don't believe you need to do such planning!

Keeping track of each Action Item and Milestone Goal through a digital, whiteboard or a paper plan of action is essential to achieving each and every one of your Big Hairy Audacious Goals. It is essential to realizing your Life Plan.

CHAPTER 21

THE ALL-IMPORTANT DAILY ACTIONS

I NEED TO talk more about those all-important Action Items.

The brain is a muscle that 'gets tired'. Or so the mind would like us to believe! Usually you can resist a temptation in the morning when you and your brain are rested, but then fail to resist temptations in the evening after a long day. In the morning, those Action Items don't seem so hard. In the late afternoon and evening, they seem like heavy lifting! But that is just your 'whiny little mind' complaining, isn't it? Yes! To get around the whining and procrastinating, you need a structure.

Structure and processes and schedules allow us to exert less energy and brain power. Structures help you short-circuit the whiny 'but I'm so exhausted' thoughts because they are No-Brainers. We just refer to something that is already set up rather than recreating the wheel every day. That way, we don't fall for the excuse that our brain is 'tired'. Because our structure is built as a no-brainer, the brain telling us that it is tired has no power over you!

Because we are always working from a **written Life Plan** and a **written Dashboard** with **written Milestone Goals** and **written Action Items** — our structure — we never need to 'wrack our brain' to figure out or remember what is next.

Look at what you wrote. Do it. Move on.

Since the structure is mapped out clearly right before your eyes, you will have **less reluctance or resistance** (no excuses) to performing the indicated actions each and every day. After a few days and weeks of doing this, it will become second nature to perform your Action Items and to note the achieved Milestones getting you closer and closer to your Big Hairy Audacious Goal attainment.

Routine

For some people I know, 'routine' is a dirty word! But for you on a Life Planning Journey, it must now be meaningful in the context of achieving your Plan. When you wake up each morning, you now know exactly what your '**start-up routine**' is. Before turning in each night, you now know exactly what your '**review-of-the-day routine**' is.

Write It

For still other people, writing anything down — this Life Plan of yours, not to mention daily lists of Action Items — is like punishment! But for you on a Life Planning Journey, writing (and regularly re-reading what you wrote) must become second nature.

To achieve your Life Plan calls for some discipline, granted. I think you agree that not all of us are as disciplined (or as 'routine-oriented') as others — or as we might need to be to achieve a long-term objective.

Let's look at ways that you can organize yourself on a daily basis to achieve all the outcomes that are part of your Life Plan.

Structure

Doing something every day towards your goals may seem obvious, but what is it that you are doing? You are:

1. Performing a **morning routine to focus you** for today's achievements.
2. Performing the written **Action Items** connected to each of your Milestones.
3. **Living** the rest of your life, just going about your business-as-usual.
4. Performing an **evening routine to review** today's achievements.

I believe that giving yourself a clear structured plan that guides what you do every day toward your BHAGs makes achieving your Life Plan and its BHAGs more effortless. The structure includes a morning and evening routine, and your Action Item list for the day.

I like to say, "When you own *your morning*, you own *your life*."

Structure — routines, processes, schedules, plans — requires less discipline.

Here is a sample of my own morning routine. Adapt it for yourself, as the examples following my own chart show you how to do.

1. Get up Early (*with a quick prayer*)
2. Read a Daily Devotional
3. Prayerful/Mindful Thinking Time, during which I remember to:
   - Make a short mental list of what I am Grateful For
   - Celebrate Accomplishments
   - Pray
   - Think About What I Want to Accomplish Today
     → (the important stuff — not just the urgent stuff)
4. 'Just Be' for 5 Minutes (Meditate; no 'fidgeting'; just me with me, quietly)
5. Journaling/Writing out:
   - What I learned
   - What I want to accomplish
   - A quote or two I want to keep with me for this day
6. Create a 'Retrospection' section to my Journal:
   - This where I think about yesterday and write down:
     → What went well
     → What I could improve on
     → What was lacking
     → What I am going to change

Example: Morning Routine

A friend of mine, as a matter of a daily action item to help reach his BHAG, takes many vitamin, mineral and food supplement tablets. He had a hard time remembering them **each morning**, a hard time remembering to do this action item. He needed a tool or a structure or a memory-jogger to make it easier.

He got inspired by a 'structure', a tool really: the daily pillbox that his mother used for her own prescription pills. He bought a 2-week, daily-compartment plastic pillbox for himself from the corner drugstore. Every other Sunday evening, he would fill the pillbox with his tablets for the coming two weeks.

It was a no-brainer each morning to know which daily compartment held his tablets, and he was less tempted to skip them. This was an action item for his health BHAG, so he was happy to have made the whole action simpler!

Example: Evening Routine

Two friends had a health BHAG (but differently worded), for which a shared Action Item was to double the exercise they performed each day and week. One had been walking one mile per day, so that became 2 miles. The other did a floor workout (only 'most' days) for 10 minutes each time, so that became a 20 minute *daily* event.

They became each other's memory-jogger and accountability partner for daily exercise.

Each evening on their respective drives home from work, they phoned and quizzed each other about yesterday's and today's successes, and the coming evening's action plan. When they skipped, it had to be a 'someone died . . . or I did' sort of reason. They could plead neither forgetfulness nor laziness!

Your Own Morning Routine

Now, in the blank chart below, fill in your morning routine as regards the actions you take *before heading off to work or doing anything else:*

My Morning Routine / Actions in Order Done

"When I own my morning, I own my life!"

A.

B.

C.

D.

E.

F.

G.

H.

I.

Setting Up Your Structure

You, too, need a **structure, a process or a memory jogger** for performing your Action Items and keeping Milestone Goals in mind that works for you all the way to the achievement not only of a Milestone or a BHAG, but your Life Plan as a whole. There are any number of ways of structuring or organizing yourself. Let's look at just three of them.

One-At-A-Time Approach

To avoid 'BHAG overwhelm', you decide to work on only one Big Hairy Audacious Goal achievement at a time.

Achieving your Life Plan is done on your timetable. I have had clients who are honestly so busy, that they have no other choice but to choose just one of their Big Hairy Audacious Goals to focus on at a time. They simply do not have any available time, for whatever reason, to take on more than just one BHAG at a time.

For other clients, writing their Life Plan has made them realize that achieving 9 out of 10 of their BHAGs depends on them achieving the 10th one first! That single BHAG was the linchpin on which achieving all the others depended (from their perspective). And so they decided to focus on that single BHAG until its achievement.

Example:

One of my clients had come to me saying, "**Nothing in my life is working for me.**" Someone had suggested that he needed to draft a Life Plan, and that I could assist.

He completed all the exercises in the Parts 1, 2 and 3 of this workbook. Just *thinking about* executing his Life Plan — full of BHAGs as you might guess — had him overwhelmed. So I asked him the question,

"If you could achieve only one really burning, really vital, Big Hairy Audacious Goal <u>in your **entire** lifetime</u>, which one would it be?"

He chose the Health Core Domain and his Priority of "getting control over heart and circulatory issues", for these reasons:

- He was starting to experience severe health issues not related to heart (he thought)
- Carrying around extra weight contributing to his health issues was exhausting and the less he did physically, the less he wanted to (could) do
- His relationships were difficult because of his physical limitations and his obsession with them
- He had little focus due to mental fuzziness and feared losing his job because of his low-grade performance; his lack of mental focus affected personal relationships, too
- He feared not being able to act or react in case of emergencies or danger, due to his non-responsive body

Now, I am the first to say that I am decidedly not a health professional! But I am a planning guide and wore this hat for this client. We formulated his BHAG statement. We set out Milestone Goals and Action Items for the first week, the first month, and the first three months.

We kept it all very short-term, **but he was still busy**. There were action items he had to do several times daily. They were a combination of gaining new knowledge, consulting expert health professionals, exercising and food-related things.

After the short-term (one-month and three-month) Milestones were achieved, he said he already felt better, and saw results. We carried on with new Milestones and the related Action Items in the same way for another period of three months, and so on.

In the meanwhile, he did not pay any attention to his other Big Hairy Audacious Goals at all, but in his words, he became a 'Health BHAG machine'. And truly? He saw measurable results every 3 months — measurable from a medical testing perspective, but also from his internal observations of himself. He had more clear-headedness, more physical energy and other positive shifts that he felt *from within*. And you know what astounded him the most? He felt HAPPIER. He felt happier straight out of bed and throughout the day. That was new for him.

With this One-BHAG-At-A-Time approach, its Milestones and corresponding Action Items are all you focus on each and every day. If this approach appeals to you, ask yourself:

"Is there one Core Domain presenting a Priority and BHAG that — once achieved — would make all my other BHAGs <u>fall into place</u> more easily?"

Or, differently stated:

"Is there one Core Domain that hurts my life much, much more than any other? Is that Core Domain in my Wheel of Life so flat that it prevents other areas from improving?"

That is the Core Domain Priority — the BHAG — you start with in this one-at-a-time approach!

Nonetheless, as specific as this seems, you need a structure to perform each day to keep you on track. Write everything down. Use a simple checklist format such as the one on the next page, or you can do this in your digital, whiteboard or paper agenda book. Also follow the 'funnel structure' I use in the next section. In this case, your daily process deals with just one BHAG. I show you how to get started — create a new chart for each successive Milestone Goal.

BHAG/Due Date: _____

1st MILESTONE/Due Date: _____

Action Item:	Completed Today?

List-Lovers Approach

This second approach is for those of you who are hooked on making lists. Nothing says not to use lists to help achieve your Life Plan! I know a number of people who cannot do anything without their lists or checklists. Here is a way to use lists to achieve your Life Plan.

The idea is to break your priorities in 6 different category lists as shown on the next page. The **#1 (Now)** list are things you are going to get done or work on **today**. This list should only have **3 items** on it — all of them related to your Life Plan's action items that you have determined are necessary to perform to achieve your current Milestone Goal. Keep going with the remaining 5 lists. Define them as you wish. Don't put more than three action items in any list. You might end up with 6 pieces of paper or 6 pages in your notebook. Or you might create something like this Master List:

#1 (Now)

A.	
B.	
C.	

#2 (Next)

A.	
B.	
C.	

#3 (Soon)

A.	
B.	
C.	

#4 (Later)

A.	
B.	
C.	

#5 (Someday)

A.	
B.	
C.	

#6 (Waiting)

A.	
B.	
C.	

The purpose of the 6 lists? They allow you to proactively prioritize your action items and know they are in a 'system'. Might you still have other lists, if you are a 'list-lover'? Sure. Continue to keep your separate grocery/shopping list, pre-vacation to-do list, etc. Make sure you know where you are keeping your 6 Life Planning lists for easy referral every day.

The **6 lists** along with the **Dashboard/One Page Life Plan™** will be the keys to success for list-lovers. The Dashboard is a good reminder of the bigger picture and should act as your dashboard the you have decided for your life. The Dashboard will be your driver for how you prioritize your action items into the proper list.

> **NOTE**: Your calendar or agenda book page for 'today' is not a list! You should not use it for writing your lists or for list tracking. Your calendar is for blocking time to work on specific action items *that are on that* list, and to book actual appointments.

This One-At-A-Time approach works for many, but there is a second approach that also works wonders.

Funnel Approach

If you have decided to go for achievement of two or more BHAG at once, you also, obviously, need to get organized to achieve them. A third way of organizing yourself to achieve many BHAGs simultaneously is the **funnel approach**.

Each and every day you start at the *top or wide end of the funnel* and work your way down it and out the spout. In other words, you start your day with 'the Big Picture' and get more and more detailed as you proceed.

The Big Picture is your Personal Mission Statement and all your Big Hairy Audacious Goal statements. You do all the items in the top, wide part of the funnel first thing in the morning. You inch down the funnel and into 'the spout' throughout the remainder of your day.

<u>Top of the funnel</u>. Morning. Read your **Personal Mission Statement** and **Big Hairy Audacious Goal statements** to yourself to start the day. Every. Single. Day.

This directs your mind to your ultimate goals. It creates a picture in your mind of where you are going. It motivates you to take a few simple actions today, because you know they are moving you toward the achievement of your ultimate goals.

Inch down the funnel. **Daily Questions.** I like to stay near the top of the funnel and position my thinking and my energy in a certain direction for the day. It's a moment of quietness for me. After a moment of quietness, I ask myself my **Daily Questions.** For me, they are the same questions every day. My questions do not have to be your questions. (*More on formulating them later.*)

Inch down the funnel. **Weekly Review.** After that, I look at my **agenda for the entire week in progress** (for me it is a screen shot of my calendar; for you it might be pages in a paper agenda book). Even if it's, say, Wednesday, I remind myself of action items I took on Monday and Tuesday, and look at items I will need to perform Thursday and Friday as well. That **situates my action items for this day**, Wednesday, in a bigger context. It makes today's action items seem ever more vital to the structure I have built for achieving my BHAG.

Inch down the funnel towards the spout. **Today's Action Items.** Now I look at today's Action Items, and the **actual time today** that I will be performing them. Some action items might be the first thing you do when you roll out of bed. Others might happen first thing at your desk. Still others might take place after work in the afternoon. You get the idea. The time of day each is done is on your schedule.

Enter the spout. **Live My Day.** I do all the action items on today's list — as scheduled, treating them like appointments. Then? I just carry on with the rest of my day before and after doing them. That means I perform my work at my job or honor work and family appointments I have made, and generally do everything in a 'normal' day that I usually do.

Out the spout. **Review the Day.** At the end of the day, when I have decided it's time to go to bed and that I am near the 'exit' end of the funnel's spout, I take a quiet break. With my **written plan in hand, I review my day**. Again, I look at my Mission Statement and Big Hairy Audacious Goals and read them to myself again. Then I look at the Action Items of today and check off the ones that I have actually performed. If it happens for any reason that I did not perform today's action items, I do a retrospective and review **"what happened?"** I work on understanding the why I didn't get that particular task done. Then I determine what I can do different to get better.

Visualize: End of evening. **See it.** When complete, I sit back comfortably, relax and quiet my mind. I do my best to visualize the Big Hairy Audacious Goals as already achieved. I visualize what my life is like when I have achieved one of them, then all of them. This usually puts a big smile on my face and I can end the day on a positive note.

Funnel Summary

From morning to night, the funnel can be summarized as 10 steps to take.

UPON WAKING:

1: Read your **Big Hairy Audacious Goals** to yourself.

2: Ask yourself your **Daily Questions**.

3: Re-read your **one-week schedule of action items for each BHAG**.

4: Read out **today's action items**, and the time of day each one is scheduled.

5: Set **appointment alarms** for each action item.

GO ABOUT YOUR DAY, AS YOU:

6: **Perform each action item as scheduled.**
Check it off your to-do list.

END-OF-DAY REVIEW:

7: **Review of all completed action items.**
Ask, "What happened?" about each outstanding item (the ones you failed to do). Can you do them now?

8: Again, ask yourself your **Five Daily Questions**.
Can you honestly answer 'Yes'?

9: Again, read your **Big Hairy Audacious Goals** to yourself.

10: Close your eyes and **visualize** your life _as if each BHAG is already achieved_.

Funneling is one way to organize yourself so that you 'execute' your Life Plan on a schedule. It is how my client whose BHAG was the PhD did it. It is how the 'dressy dress' was ready in plenty of time for the family event. It is how that client's 40 pounds were lost, right on time.

The Daily Questions

Counteracting your excuses and procrastination **for not doing the action items** is part of your job. Unless (and even if) you have an accountability partner, you are on your own to do the action items, and stick to your plan.

Part of the structure that I gave you above is called **The Daily Questions**. These are five or more questions that help you keep on track and performing the action items that are part of your Milestones, your BHAGs and your Life Plan. Each question starts with the words, "Did I do my best to . . ." The question is formulated so that it can only be answered with Yes or No. The answer to each question must be Yes for you to count it as a success. If not, you have work to do!

Marshall Goldsmith is (as far as I know) the originator of this idea, and a sample of questions you might choose to ask yourself each day follows below. Marshall Goldsmith gives himself up to 32 questions; I recommend at least five. I set my own questions to keep me positive and focused all day. Others set their questions to keep them from procrastinating. The questions are your personal choice, but I recommend that you set them for yourself within the context of "doing what it takes to achieve my Life Plan".

Sample Questions:

"Did I do my best to . . .
1. set clear goals [tasks; objectives] for my day?"
2. make progress — by completing my Action Items — toward MILESTONE/ BHAG achievement?"
3. be happy, whatever is going on around me?"
4. create positive, meaningful interactions with everyone?"
5. focus and be fully engaged with tasks and people?"

Exercise

Write some of your own Daily Questions below. Over the next week or two, come back to refine, change, add/remove some, until you have a list that you can use every day, over the long-term.

My Daily Questions

"Did I do my best to . . .

CHAPTER 22

REVIEW OF
EXECUTION TOOLS

EARLIER, I SHOWED you some ways you could write or print out your Life Plan on one page — thus creating a One Page Life Plan™. You'll modify it each year, 'erasing' those BHAG or Milestone Goals achieved and adding in the new ones for the coming year.

I will always encourage you to adopt a system that allows you to track your Goal-Producing Action Items and what has been completed. The key is to have a <u>trusted system</u> where you can continually prioritize your Goal-Producing Action Items as they get intermingled with all of the activities of daily life that are not directly related to achievement of your BHAG.

As we've discussed, there are manual ways, along with digital ways, of tracking your Life Plan. The key is to have a consistent system that you can trust . . . and that you know you will use every day. This will allow you continually work on the important action items, not just the urgent action items of the day or week.

The importance of having a trusted system where your action items, your BHAG and Milestone Goal statements, and anything you have to do is 'memorialized' in a safe place. If you have your action items written out and safely stored but available to you, it frees up your mind to focus on the current activity. If you are trying to remember things without having written it out, your mind has to switch back and forth; it really is tiresome and inefficient.

Your mind is a great place to create things,
but a terrible place to hold them.

Let's review Low and High Tech Tools to get you organized on your journey. Whichever way you go, the key is to be consistent. Knowledge of processes and systems can be very useful, but if not consistently applied, they will be useless. I repeat — the tools and system you choose must work <u>for you</u>.

Low Tech Tools

Notebooks made of paper! Pens, pencils! You cannot get more 'old school' than that. This would naturally include formal agenda books like a Day Timer or Filofax. It could be as easy as a drugstore student notebook of any size you like.

Example:

One client of mine is quite low-tech. Though she is computer-literate, she is a pen-and-paper lover. She always prefers to write everything out by hand. She was one of the first adopters of the 1980s fad of Filofax agendas, and I've always known her to have a stash of pens and pencils, notepads, and her ever-present bound paper Annual Agenda book. She uses it to map her daily routine — literally recopying it every week. She schedules her Milestone Action Items like appointments, by writing them in specific times of each day's page. You get the idea.

Additional to that, at home she kept a giant paper list on her wall of BHAG/Due Dates to be achieved, with the Milestone Goals/Due Dates written under each one. Her greatest joy was to cross them off when attained! Since handwriting was a comfortable pattern of hers, it was also a reliable way for her to track her Life Plan.

Paper . . . Plus Audio

Some stay low tech, but recognize the efficiency of technology when it works for their style.

Example:

A second client of mine was an attorney. He was resolutely computer-stupid (his phrase). He couldn't type on a keyboard to save his life. His decision not to learn computers at all led him to reorganizing his work and his life (imagine raising children who scoff at your computer illiteracy . . . but that didn't faze him) differently than most folks today.

His big 'high-tech' tool is a little audio recorder. He uses it to audio record himself for every aspect of his work, and gives that audio to his secretary for keyboarding (she has her own processes for doing that and he doesn't concern himself with them).

He currently uses the same process to track his life plan — but for privacy, it is his spouse who keeps the *written parts* all straight for him.

This is another, sort of low-tech approach to executing and tracking a Life Plan which is totally dependable for you . . . if this is your style.

Paper . . . Plus Sticky Index Cards

I work with technology quite a bit. Even when I do strategy sessions with my teams and get everything in an electronic format — whether it is Excel, Word or some application we have decided to use — there is a downside to it. ***It can easily become 'out-of-sight-out-of-mind'***. It's not visible all day long for us. It's not 'in our face' unless we sit all day in front of the computer monitor with just that plan on the screen. And who does that? No one. Plan execution becomes problematical.

One very cool thing we adopted was using **3x5 sticky index cards**. Here is how we use them:

1. We create cards for the 6 priority lists categories and put them on the wall across the top.
2. Then we create cards for each action item and put them in order in the correct priority bucket.
3. We also created a completed card so when that action item card is completed, you put it in the completed column.
4. Every day the cards should be adjusted into the proper priority bucket and order.
5. Eventually you will have to start stacking the completed cards on the floor!

This creates a visualized momentum for us, to prove that we are getting things done.

NOTE: *Take a picture everyday of your wall of priorities,*
so you have it with you all the time.

High Tech Tools

Very mobile people today like the convenience of 'carrying it all around' on their smartphone or tablet. There are many software apps to download, tools to help facilitate the accomplishing of all your daily tasks that lead you toward your goals and BHAG(s). Technology has made it easy for you to have access to all the tools you need to help keep yourself accountable. By using all your devices — like phones, tablets, or computers — with a few new applications, you can optimize yourself for Life Plan execution.

To get started, I recommend using two apps: *OneNote* by Microsoft and *Wunderlist*. This said, there are many other task-tracking apps out there so feel free to adopt the methods to the apps you are comfortable with.

Let's see how to use both my preferred apps, because remember that it is not enough to download an app! You need to learn to use, and then . . . actually use it! Experiment with and test several apps if you need to.

Wunderlist Setup

1. Download the app
2. Setup an account with username and password
3. Select the option in the app to "Create List"
4. Create 6 Lists (you recognize these from a prior section)
   - 1-Now
   - 2-Next
   - 3-Soon
   - 4-Later
   - 5-Someday
   - 6-Waiting
5. Add an action item to the 1-Now list
6. Fill in the details of the action item with the functions of Wunderlist
   - It has due date, reminders, subtasks, notes, and attach files functions if you need them
7. Add all your action items to each list, remember the 1-Now list should only have 3 items in it.
8. Practice moving action items from one list to another
   - Depending on your device, this may function differently, but you need to know this functionality because you will be reviewing your action items daily
9. Use this for 30 days and adjust as needed
10. When you complete an item, hit the checkbox to the left
    - Note it keeps the completed list and just hides them
    - At the bottom of the screen it will allow you to see completed items if you would like

This setup will allow you to add action items that come up during the day, so you don't have to try to remember them. You will probably end up adding a few other lists. That's perfectly fine, especially if you are a list-driven person!

A few non-Life-Plan lists are:

- Shopping (ongoing grocery list)
- Vacation wish list or pre-vacation to-do items
- Movies to watch for in theaters
- Restaurants to try
- Christmas gift ideas, so I'm not at a loss for what to get at the 11th hour

Remember to stop trying to remember things! That sounds crazy? Not really. Just use memory tools that are out there. Use lists so you can focus on your BHAGs. This is a key to execution and productivity.

<u>NOTE</u>: *You can share lists with your partner, kids or whoever you want. Sharing our shopping list was a huge time saver for my wife and kids.*

OneNote Setup

1. Download the app
2. Setup an account with username and password
3. Create a New Notebook — Call it "Action Items"
4. Create 7 New Sections at the Top with the Following (use the + sign)
   - 1-Now
   - 2-Next
   - 3-Soon
   - 4-Later
   - 5-Someday
   - 6-Waiting
   - 7-Completed

An example screenshot from one of my own OneNote notebooks.

5. Add an action item to 1-Now Section
    *   Click on the "Add Page" + sign)
6. Give it a Title and type details of your action item
    *   Note that you can have multiple text boxes, pictures, drawings, voice recordings on your 1st page
7. Add all your action items to the appropriate priority list/section.
8. Practice dragging and dropping action items from one page to another
9. Use for 30 Days
    *   When items are completed, simply drag that page/action item to the 'completed' tab
10. Tips
    *   You can take pictures from your phone just by clicking the camera icon when you are in a note
    *   Watch a YouTube on how to use OneNote. There are plenty of good free training YouTubes out there.
    *   If you use Outlook — there is a OneNote icon that will instantly convert an email with any attachments to OneNote so you don't have to manage that tasks from Outlook/Email.

These are just two apps that work for me. Ask around to see what your friends and associates use. Google 'planning apps' and see what looks interesting.

Choose and Commit

Choose a structure. Commit to it. Refer, refer, and refer again to it all day long and stay focused on those BHAG-producing Milestone Goals and Action Items.

You can do it.

CONCLUSION

YOU HAVE COME to know yourself much, much better through the Awareness Exercises I have presented. I hope you have not skipped any of them! If so, don't beat yourself up and don't roll your eyes at me (hey, I've raised children!).

Go back now and do them all — or just do them *again,* with more focus and attention than that first time 'round. Added to each other, the exercises will flesh out and clarify what you want to do and give you more tools to go through life than you can ever guess.

Doing these exercises confirms or reveals to you two important bits of information:

Who you are.
How you are wired to succeed in life.

Here's another gem that it took me a long time to understand:

It only takes one person — YOU — making these personal incremental changes to create a massively positive change in all your relationships.

What do I mean? If you are in a committed relationship, I can guarantee that even if your partner does not do this work with you for him/herself, your relationship with that individual will improve! This will be true of all your relationships! Wow! All it takes is for one person (you) to develop more self-awareness and start working for personal improvement . . . to see all your interactions with others improve as well. How? They will hold less drama, be much more harmonious. You will find just talking with each other more comfortable and natural. You'll all be happier.

If you are in a committed relationship, having done this work might show you the power of both of you joining forces to create a Couple's Life Plan. I have processes that help you work through such planning — watch my website for news on that workbook, being released soon!

Live Intentionally

Is this all 'new and improved me' an overnight thing? No, my friend. But shifts will nonetheless start occurring on the very day you commit <u>mentally</u> to self-improvement and life improvement. You know that old saying, "I was an overnight success. All it took was 20 years." Well, it won't take you that long! But stick with it. Commit to yourself. Make appointments with yourself. Do this. Perform those Action Items. No one I know of who has made such a determined and focused commitment to improvement has ever regretted it.

The biggest regret people have in life is — They didn't do what they wanted to do and did what everyone else told them to do. Decide Now — That is all it takes.

Indeed, my mission is to guide people toward ways that work for them to **live their lives intentionally**. A Life Plan is a declaration of <u>intention</u>, isn't it? Setting Big Hairy Audacious Goals is a systematic way for stretching yourself and reaching more of your <u>potential</u>, isn't it?

My life mission is to help others be better than they thought. My BHAG is to influence 100,000 people do a life plan AND maximize their true **potential**. When you do your life plan and complete your One Page Life Plan™, please visit my website and let me know. I am working on my BHAG and you are part of it. I invite you to keep returning to my website at **www.craigsroda.com** for new life tips and tools.

I WISH YOU ALL THE BEST
AS YOU CREATE THE
BEST VERSION OF YOU!!!

LIST OF RESOURCES

As you continue your journey in creating and living an intentional life, you might like to revisit some of the resources and to do some further reading. Below is a list of resources that were either presented as chapter exercises or were briefly mentioned in the book.

Online Assessments

- *StrengthsFinder 2.0* by Clifton/Gallup Research. **www.strengthsfinder.com**
- *16 Personalities* by NERIS Analytics Limited. **www.16personalities.com**
- *Emotional Intelligence Free EQ Quiz* by The Institute for Health and Human Potential (IHHP). **www.ihhp.com/free-eq-quiz**
- *Emotional Intelligence Test* by PsychTests AIM Inc. **http://testyourself.psychtests.com/testid/3038**
- Full DISC Assessment by Robbins Research International, Inc. **www.tonyrobbins.com/disc**
- Time Management Assessment by Mind Tools. **www.mindtools.com/pages/article/newHTE_88.htm**

Books & Authors

- **Gary Chapman,** author of *The 5 Love Languages: The Secret to Love that Lasts*
- **Jim Collins,** author of *Good to Great: Why Some Companies Make the Leap and Others Don't*
- **Peter Drucker,** author of *Managing Oneself*
- **Stephen Covey,** author of *The 7 Habits of Highly Effective People: Powerful Lessons in Personal Change*
- **Tony Robbins,** author of *Awaken The Giant Within*

Podcasts

Leadership, Business, Personal Growth
From Dave Ramsey
www.entreleadership.com

Faith
From Andy Stanley
www.yourmove.is

General Learning
From TED Talks
TED Radio Hour
www.npr.org/podcasts

ABOUT THE AUTHOR

CRAIG SRODA co-founded and served as CEO of Pinnacle of Indiana for 18 years. Pinnacle was one of the largest Microsoft Partners in Northern Indiana helping companies develop their technology strategy. His strengths are understanding and aligning technology with business goals through his whiteboarding strategy sessions. His passion is helping individuals operate in their "sweet spot"— a place where their passion and strengths intersect so they can maximize their potential.

Craig's previous books include *You in the Sweet Spot* and *Intentional Living and Leadership. You in the Sweet Spot* introduces tools to help individuals garner a deeper understanding about themselves, their purpose and their "sweet spot" so they can live on purpose with purpose.

After completing his first Life Plan and exposing priorities of his faith, his wife, three daughters, and wanting to help others live on purpose, he sold his company. After many mistakes and learning opportunities on his journey, he is committed to helping others recognize their natural strengths, know their WHY, and helping them complete their own life plan so they can live on purpose and minimize regrets.

For more information, visit **www.CraigSroda.com**

Made in the USA
Monee, IL
14 December 2019